WRAP® Plus

by
Mary Ellen Copeland, Ph.D.

Portions of this book are based on work previously published in
Living Without Depression and Manic Depression

Advocates for Human Potential, Inc.

WRAP® and Wellness Recovery Action Plan® are trademarks of Advocates for Human Potential, Inc.

Cover design by Joan Copeland

Printed in the United States of America

ISBN: 978-0-9795560-8-1

ISBN 978-097955608-1

9 780979 556081

Kathryn Strouse Copeland

January 7, 1912 — April 5, 1994

This book is dedicated to the memory of my mother, Kathryne Strouse Copeland, my guide, inspiration and support, who has shown me and thousands of others that there is hope, that we can take back our lives, that there is light at the end of the tunnel. Because of her, "hopeless" means "hope." And "incurably insane" means "That's what *you* think." Her courage and strength have paved the way for each of us.

In 1949, she was hospitalized in a state mental hospital for major depression. For eight long years she lived in that hospital, as her moods alternated from deep depression to extreme mania. We were told to forget her, that she would never get well.

My mother got well. The extreme moods ceased. She came home. She spent the rest of her life, 37 years, living to the fullest – working as a dietitian in the New Haven, Connecticut school system for 20 years, babysitting for her grandchildren and great-grandchildren, cooking for everyone, supporting her family and friends. She became a highly respected and much loved member of the community.

She has a huge network of family, friends, and people she inspired. We will all miss her, but her message of courage and hope will never be forgotten.

Contents

Foreword

Author's note: *This was written when the first version of this book was originally published in 1994. I have added an update at the end.*

A few days ago, as I was watching the news on television, the commentator mentioned it was the anniversary of a historic event. I vividly recalled that event, where I was living, what I was doing and what I was feeling like at the time. I was one of several younger people who, because of their "disabilities," were living in a housing complex for the elderly. So there I was, at the age of 47, living in a high-rise apartment building where the average age of the other residents was at least several decades more than mine, and where there were many special accommodations to meet the needs of the residents.

My brain felt like it was filled with sticky, gauzy cobwebs. If someone asked me a question, I couldn't remember it long enough to answer. The simplest mathematics problem, like adding two months' phone bills, had me stumped. I moved slowly, managing to accomplish in a day the bare minimum of tasks to get by. I was overweight. My hair and skin were coarse and dry. My connections with the world were minimal, limited to a few close friends and persistent family members who had "stayed the course." I spent a lot of time watching mindless programs on television while wishing for an end to the horror my life had become.

I had experienced mental health difficulties for as long as I could remember, but had always managed to get by. In 1986 these issues became overpowering, taking over my life. My moods alternated from months of severe "highs" with spending sprees, bizarre behavior, impulsive, destructive decision making and actions, to deep, black sadness where I was unable to think or to feel, where I felt dead inside. These erratic mood swings persisted in spite of several hospitalizations, doctors who searched diligently for the right combination of medications and counselors who were supportive and persistent through one crisis after another.

It was during this time that I asked my doctor how people with diagnoses like mine get by on a day-to-day basis. He said he would get me that information. I looked forward with anticipation to our next visit. When I asked for the information, he said there wasn't any.

I explained my dilemma to a vocational rehabilitation counselor, and, with her support, I slowly, through the fog, began my study of how people with mental health challenges get by on a day-to-day basis.

There were 120 people in my first study. When their responses to my questionnaire started pouring into my mailbox, I felt overwhelmed. I had no idea how I was ever going to take this gold mine of information and assemble it into a useful document, much less put any of the suggestions into practice in my own life.

It was at that time, when I felt I had really hit the bottom with lots of good work to do and no energy or enthusiasm to do it, that thankfully, things started to change.

First, several doctors suggested I try light therapy to treat my horrible, but predictable, deep winter sadness. I bought an inexpensive shop light fixture, replaced the fluorescent bulbs with full spectrum light bulbs and set it on the table to light my living room while I watched TV and made efforts to compile the study data. I noticed that I started to feel better. My mind began to clear. I could work on the data for longer periods of time. I found this interesting and even a little exciting. I decided to buy two more shop light fixtures and four more full spectrum bulbs, talked my son into mounting them on a piece of plywood and I had myself a primitive but effective light box. The more I used it the better I felt.

This new energy gave me the spark I needed to incorporate into my life some of the strategies suggested in the study, and which I later described in my first book, *The Depression Workbook: A Guide to Living with Depression and Manic Depression*. My level of wellness and stability continued to improve.

While making these changes a doctor encouraged me to see an endocrinologist, as he felt my puffy appearance, dry skin and hair, slow movement and inability to tolerate cold indicated that I might have a thyroid disorder. The endocrinologist found that I did indeed have severe hypothyroidism, perhaps because I had been taking lithium for many years. With treatment of that condition and the resulting increases in energy, stamina and concentration, I began to feel that there was a light at the end of the tunnel and that perhaps my life, as I used to know it, was not over as I had feared, a fear shared by family members and friends.

My healing and recovery have continued. I still have mornings, fewer and fewer though, where I want to stay in bed with the covers over my head, curled up in a fetal position. But the work I have to do, and the promises I have to keep, get me up and going. There are other days when I feel as if I am going so fast that my feet aren't touching the floor, my heart is pounding and ideas are whirling around in my head faster than the speed of sound. That's when I know I have to curtail my activities, decrease the stimulation, calm myself down, do some relaxation exercises and take a slow walk in the woods.

Is it easy? Never. I have to meet the challenge of keeping myself balanced on a daily basis. I have to use every ounce of my creative, innovative energies to find coping mechanisms and solutions that keep me stable. Some days I feel as if I am climbing a 1500 foot vertical cliff on a hot, muggy day, searching for crevices for my hands and feet to make my way to the shelter at the top before the encroaching lightning storm sends me crashing into the abyss. Other days it's like walking barefoot across a field of gently undulating sand dunes in the sunshine on a warm spring day.

In the years since 1992, I have experienced the most traumatic events of my entire life, events that threatened to tear away the very underpinnings of my soul. I keep going, one moment at a time, one foot firmly planted in front of the other.

Could I have made it without the safety net provided by my ever-growing circle of close friends and family? No way. This mutually supportive network is now pleasantly supplemented for me by a phone call or letter from someone somewhere in the country with comments like the following:

"Recently I purchased a copy of The Depression Workbook. I am very impressed by all the compassionate, hard work that has gone into this publication, as well as the considerable knowledge regarding depression. I believe this workbook would be very helpful to the many patients that I and my colleagues work with on the psychiatric unit..."

"What a great job ! I can easily see that you put a ton of work into this project. Thank you for sharing the results with us!"

"What a wonderful workshop! The clients and I learned so much!"

"Too bad you didn't have hours to talk and an hour to answer questions!"

Addendum

In the years since I first set that shop light fixture on my living room table, I have completed six major research projects, written and published many books, including four major recovery curriculums, developed audio and video resources, written on-line courses and developed a recovery website. I have given numerous presentations, to thousands of people all around the country. I have led workshops at national and statewide conferences for people who live with mental health challenges on a day-to-day basis, their family members and supporters. I have presented to health care providers about the information people with mental health challenges really need. I have led numerous Mental Health Recovery and WRAP trainings, and WRAP group facilitator trainings, both in the United States and around the world. I now have a doctor's degree, earned through intensive study of mental health recovery innovations. I not only have my life back, but the possibilities seem endless.

In addition, I have made many significant changes in lifestyle and attitude, too many to mention here. The key changes include:

I now live in a bright, cheery, comfortable, easy to maintain space where I have privacy.

I limit the time that I spend working on serious (and potentially depressing) life issues, such as the effects of childhood abuse and low self-esteem caused by years of mental illness labeling, to counseling sessions and exchange listening sessions. I have chosen to focus the rest of the time on my work, the things I enjoy doing and the things I appreciate about being alive. I would rather spend my time doing things like reading a good book, taking a walk, petting my dog, working on a quilt, bird-watching, playing with a grandchild or cross-country skiing — Wellness Tools.

I have given up my workaholic style. I understand that I have the right to have fun and plan some pleasurable activity in every day.

I take good care of myself. I watch my diet carefully, exercise almost daily, use my light box whenever the days are dark and dreary, and I reach out for assistance to a team of health care experts whenever I have health problems that are difficult to solve.

My new career, which I have developed myself, has a flexible schedule and makes optimum use of my abilities and talents.

For the first time in my life I feel closely connected to and loved by many wonderful people. I have a strong network of family and local support. In addition, I am blessed with a broader network of people from all over the country and all over the world who support me in my work and life.

The most important change of all is that I want to live. I treasure this wonderful life I have made for myself. Each day is a new adventure. My outlook on the future is bright and clear.

About this Book

Since I began my studies of people who experience mental health challenges, I have traveled extensively around the country and around the world, presenting workshops and lectures to thousands of people who have experienced mental health difficulties or support someone who does. I have met many outstanding people who have been told they have severe and persistent mental illness, and that they can never expect to get better, and may even get worse over time. Many of these people have gotten well and stayed well for long periods of time. From time to time they may have noticed that they were not doing as well as they wished. Then they did what they needed to do to bring themselves back to wellness.

These people work, take care of family responsibilities, and do the things they enjoy. This intrigued me. I wanted to find out how they get well and stay well. And I wanted to share this information with others who are searching for answers. People should not have to live with a diagnosis and issues that frequently lead to invalidation, unemployment, low self-esteem, limited support, and severed connections. They should not be kept from being the people they want to be, doing the things they want to do, and reaching their life goals.

How To Use This Book

This book is written in workbook style. It provides an opportunity to explore more intensively the various ideas presented. Many people report that completing the exercises in my first book, *The Depression Workbook: A Guide to Living with Depression and Manic Depression*, has been very helpful. You may choose not to do the exercises or to do only those that are appropriate to your circumstance. It's your choice. Whatever you feel will work best for you is the right thing to do.

This is your book. You may feel inhibited by writing exercises. It may remind you of elementary school workbooks where everything had to be neat, tidy, and spelled correctly, using proper punctuation and grammar. That is not the case with this book. Forget the old rules. Write whatever you feel like, any way that it comes out.

While the book is meant to be used in its entirety, each chapter stands on its own to facilitate use. References are made in individual chapters to related information in other chapters.

I suggest you read the book through and then return to the chapters that are most appropriate to your needs. For instance, many of us have thoroughly explored medical issues, but need to focus on resolving life issues that are interfering with our recovery and wellness.

As with *The Depression Workbook*, the format of this book is appropriate and recommended for use by educational and support groups. You can cover a section or a chapter at each session. Or participants can review the chapter or section in advance, and it can be discussed in the group.

What is in This Book

The book begins with a chapter on Self-advocacy. In order to work on your recovery, you need to be responsible for your own wellness and be willing and able to advocate effectively for what you need. The process of finding out if your difficulties might have medical causes is addressed in the chapter, "Medical Considerations." If your physician prescribes medications, read the chapter on issues dealing with medication use and management. The life assessment chapter gives you an opportunity to explore your life experiences to see if there are experiences or issues that are getting in the way of your wellness. If these issues are factors, subsequent chapters will present ideas that are useful in relieving such circumstances. Several chapters describe lifestyle and wellness strategies essential to achieving a healthy balance.

In addition, this book will guide you through the process of developing your personal Wellness Recovery Action Plan®. WRAP® includes the Wellness Toolbox, the Daily Maintenance Plan, Triggers and an Action Plan, Early Warning Signs and an Action Plan, When Things are Breaking Down and an Action Plan, a Crisis Plan and Post Crisis Planning.

Who Will Benefit from Using This Book

This book is for anyone who experiences mental health challenges and for those people who love and support them. The strategies described in this book are useful and safe for anyone to use. They are complementary to other treatment protocols. You may choose to use medication as a Wellness Tool in addition to the other strategies described in this book.

This book includes recommendations and ideas from people who have experienced mental health challenges. I gathered this information through my ongoing study of the coping skills and wellness strategies of people who experience these kinds of challenges. You may find some of them to be helpful for you.

Everyone has ups and downs in their lives. Some days you may feel better than others. You may be able to figure out why you feel worse on some days. Maybe it's cloudy, you need to deal with problems you don't really want to deal with, several things haven't gone well, something bad has happened that is upsetting, you feel stressed with too much to do, or you are feeling badly about yourself. Sometimes you may not be able to identify why it is you don't feel right. Other days, when things are going well, or for no apparent reason, you feel great. You sing in the shower, there is a bounce to your step as you walk along, and you feel good. This is normal.

For some of us, our ongoing "ups and downs" are so severe and pronounced that they get in the way of every facet of our lives, destroying relationships, careers and dreams.

Take advantage of those times when you feel really good to learn the new techniques and new strategies (Wellness Tools) described in this book. Then they will be easier for you to use when you are having a more difficult time.

The techniques described in this book are simple, safe, non-invasive, and for the most part, inexpensive. They can be used to effectively complement the other treatments and strategies of your choice.

Simple but Not Easy

Simple does not mean easy. Simple means not complex. Many of the techniques described in this book, like journaling, focusing and peer counseling, with a little practice, are easy to use. The more difficult part is incorporating these strategies into your life on a regular basis. It takes dedication, consistency, and persistence. Like others, you may tend to start out on new paths with enthusiasm and high expectations. But as you settle back into your routines, it is easy to slip out of the habit of practicing these techniques or to revert to old, deeply ingrained and more comfortable habits that get in the way of achieving balance. Developing and using a Wellness Recovery Action Plan ® (WRAP®), as described in this book, will help keep you on track.

Long Term

This book describes both small and bigger steps you can take toward a lifestyle that enhances wellness and stability. Occasionally when people use the tools and strategies described in this book, like WRAP®, they may experience some immediate profound relief. For instance, a day or two of light therapy can make an amazing difference that is easily felt and perceived. More often, people notice that they gradually feel better, they are having more good days and fewer bad days, and there is more good time than bad.

Safe

Safe means that the techniques and strategies described in this book, if used as described, are not harmful. Hopefully, they will be beneficial. When you use more invasive strategies like medications, the risks need to be weighed against the benefits. A good physician and other health care providers, and your supporters, can assist you making those decisions.

You may want to tell your health care providers that you are working with this book. They may be able to provide you with additional information and support.

Cost

Most of the strategies described in this book are inexpensive or without direct monetary cost. Relaxation exercises, physical exercise, peer counseling, support groups and making lifestyle changes are free. You may want to buy resource books, tapes or videos, attend lectures or seminars or get professional consultation, but the techniques are free and can be used without any additional expense.

Some techniques, like counseling, can be more expensive. To be a counselor takes many years of education. The overhead costs of maintaining an office are high. Counseling sessions, which may be necessary on a weekly basis, may cost up to $125 an hour. Many counselors have sliding scales to make their services available to more people. Even with sliding scales, people who have not been able to work consistently, or have high expenses in other areas, may find counseling costs prohibitive.

Many health insurance and health care plans limit the number of visits to counselors and other health care providers, or don't cover them at all. They often use arbitrary standards that are not relative to the needs of the person seeking services. Advocate for health care systems that allow people to get as much help as they need, when they need it, and from the health care providers of their choice.

What's Not Covered in This Book

Medications and other medical treatments, except issues dealing with management and side effects, are outside the scope of this book. If considering the use of these treatments, educate yourself about the proposed treatment by asking questions and reading literature that expresses a variety of viewpoints. Read the pharmaceutical insert that comes with the medication. Attend informational sessions and support groups.

Information can be found at general libraries or libraries at medical or psychiatric facilities. The internet is also an excellent source of information on medications and treatments you might be considering. If you are unable to research the medication or treatment that is being suggested, ask trusted members of your support team to do it for you.

This research process helps you to make good decisions on your own behalf and to ask appropriate questions of health care team members. Your life and what you do with your body is up to you. You have a right to decide what you are willing, or not willing, to put in your body or what you will allow, or not allow, to be done to your body.

This book does not address the genetic, biological, psychological, or environmental controversy about the origin of mental health issues. Again, there are many books by highly qualified authors and information on the internet that covers these topics. For our purposes in this book, the origin does not matter. This book deals only with helping you get well and stay well so you can be the kind of person you want to be, feel the way you want to feel, and do the things you want to do.

The Depression Workbook: A Guide to Living with Depression and Manic Depression

The Depression Workbook: A Guide to Living with Depression and Manic Depression, my first book, is based on my original study of 120 people who have mental health issues. It contains a step-by-step program for recovery and wellness (WRAP®). You may want to use it to supplement your work in this book. You can order it and other mental health recovery resources at www.mentalhealthrecovery.com.

Keys to Recovery

Hope, Personal Responsibility, Education

For many years I felt overpowered by various feelings (anxiety, depression, mania, irritability). Over time, these feelings had taken a strong hold on my life. They overpowered me. I felt myself shrinking down into a black hole. But there was something in me that didn't want to sink into that black hole, felt there must be some way out of this, and that somehow I could get to a place where the sun was shining. And I felt strongly that the way out would be guided by others who had similar feelings and who had found their ways to the sunshine.

I began to have a dream, a dream that I would reach out to lots of others and learn from them how they overcame these feelings and found their way to wonderful new lives. I shared this dream with a vocational counselor. Together we devised a strategy to gather this information. It included surveying volunteers who would share the experiences, skills, and strategies that had been helpful to them in rebuilding their lives. It seemed like a pipe dream at the time. How could I really do this? I felt terrible most of the time. And I was lacking in self-confidence and motivation.

In spite of my feelings that I could never work toward achieving this dream, much less accomplish it, with the encouragement of my counselor, I applied for and got funding to do a study of 125 volunteers, from all over the country, to learn how they cope with the same kinds of feelings I was experiencing. Developing the surveys, sending them out, and reviewing the data took great reserves of energy that I didn't have much of in those days. But little by little, I compiled the findings.

The first thing that really stood out for me as I compiled the data, was that the people who were recovering, who were getting their lives back, doing the things they wanted to do, and being the way they wanted to be, all had HOPE. They had a vision of the future that was positive and they were working toward making it reality.

Back when I first wrote this book, it was common for people who sought treatment for mental health issues to be told that they would never get better, that they might get worse as they aged, and that they would need to take their prescribed medications for the rest of their lives. This was devastating to many people. They just "gave up," letting go of their hopes and dreams for the future. This made things even worse. Now it is well known that those dire predictions are not true. People do get well, and stay well for long periods of time. Often the mental health issues become "non-issues." They do the things they want to do with their lives.

I was told that I would never get better, and, that over time, I would probably get worse. And I was told that my mental health difficulties would increase in severity, particularly since I had bad side effects from most of the many medications that were prescribed for me. My adult children were told that they would have to "look after me." I was not happy with this prognosis. I knew that my mother had gotten well, and stayed well, after eight years in a state hospital, in the days before there were any medications and only limited treatments. I believed that there were lots more people like my mother who had left their mental health challenges behind and gone on to lead rich and productive lives. And I found out that what I believed was true. That is what I am doing. And now, fifteen years later, given WRAP and the new focus on recovery, more and more people are getting well and staying well.

Often people will say to me, "I feel so awful. How can I be hopeful?" The following exercises will help you hold the hope for your own recovery until it becomes a reality.

1. Develop a Wellness Recovery Action Plan (WRAP) and use it as your guide to daily living. (See the next section of this book for instructions.)

2. Repeat these affirmations over and over whenever you can.
    "Every day in every way I am getting better and better and better."
    "People like me get well, stay well and do the things they want to with their lives."
Develop other hopeful affirmations and repeat them over and over.

_____

_____

3. Read recovery stories in the book, The WRAP Story, available online at www.mentalhealthrecovery. com, and at www.wraparoundtheworld.com. Read stories of famous, highly accomplished people who also have had mental health challenges.

4. Make lists of things and people that give you a sense of hope, like small children, nature, and special people.

_____

_____

_____

_____

5. List your hopes and dreams for your life.

Hopes and dreams

_____

First step to make it happen

_____

Hopes and dreams

_____

First step to make it happen

_____

Hopes and dreams

_____

First step to make it happen

_____

Hopes and dreams

_____

First step to make it happen

_____

6. If someone tells you there is no hope, that you will not get better, tell them that it is not helpful for them to do that, that people do get well and stay well, and that it would be more helpful to you and others if they would give positive messages of hope and support.

7. Do the activities in the "Self-Esteem" chapter of this book.

Believing that there is hope for recovery and for working toward meeting personal goals is often difficult for people who have been told they can never get well. There is now research that proves that people who have mental health challenges can, and do, get well and move on with their lives. There is lots of hope. Many, many people, even those who had the most serious difficulties, have achieved a high level of wellness.

When people start to believe in hope, they can also realize that a better life is achievable. As we begin to feel hopeful about one thing, that can lead to feeling possible about something else, and soon the quality of our lives can start to improve. Hope means that we always have options. Once we start taking some actions for ourselves, the quality of our lives can steadily get better.

Personal Responsibility

As I began analyzing the data from my early studies, I noticed an interesting phenomenon. I discovered that I could have divided the survey responses into two piles. One would have been surveys from people who were saying things like:

- "If only my mother would help out I wouldn't be having all this trouble."
- "If my father hadn't had that awful accident I would be OK."
- "If my husband would come home on time every day, I would be OK."
- "I would be OK if my kids didn't argue so much."

These people weren't getting any better. They often reported that they had gotten worse over time. The other pile of responses would have been from people who said things like:

- "I have made some changes in my diet and that has really helped me."
- "I am going to counseling every week and have joined a support group."
- "I insisted my doctor order the test that I learned I needed."
- "I am working hard on changing all these negative thoughts to positive ones."
- "I include doing things I enjoy in my plans for each day."

These people, the ones who were taking responsibility for their own lives, were getting well, and staying well, over time.

The message is clear – no matter what influence you feel others may have had over your life, your recovery journey will be much more successful if you take personal responsibility for yourself and your life.

Think about it. Do you blame everyone else for your hard time? _____
If so, it will make your recovery much easier if you can let go of that blame. One way to do that is to develop positive scenarios that contradict the "blaming" thoughts and practice them over time. For example:

Instead of saying to yourself, "My husband is always late and that upsets me," you could say to yourself, "With my husband's job, it is often hard to know when he will get home. While I am waiting, I will occupy myself with reading a good book or working on one of my writing projects. When he gets home I will welcome him and enjoy the time with him."

Instead of saying to yourself: "My doctor never orders the tests I want," you could say: "The next time I go to the doctor, I am going to take information that proves why I need the requested test. Then I am going to insist that he order the test. If he refuses, I will get a second opinion."

If you have been saying: "My kids are always fighting and it makes me upset," you could say: "Kids do tend to argue a lot. I am going to go to parenting classes and talk to my counselor to see how I can deal with this." You get the idea of what I mean. Now think about your life. Are there ways that you blame others and/or avoid taking action on your own behalf? If so, list those times, along with actions you will initiate to take personal responsibility in these situations.

Times when I blame others and/or avoid taking action on my behalf:	How I am going to deal with this:
_____	_____
_____	_____
_____	_____
_____	_____
_____	_____

Developing a Wellness Recovery Action Plan (WRAP) for yourself and using it as your guide to daily living, and using wellness tools like counseling, exchange listening, focusing, and journaling can also help you take personal responsibility for yourself and your life.

Education

When you are dealing with mental health challenges in your own life, educate yourself about the possible causes of these issues, and what can be done to relieve and eliminate them. If you are having a difficult time and can't do this for yourself, ask a trusted supporter to do this for you. (See the chapter on "Support".)

When you reach out for help, others will give you ideas on what to do. They may even insist you do what they tell you to do. Before taking any action, or using any treatment, check it out or have your supporter check it out. Find out as much as you can. Ask your physician for printed information. Go on the internet and find out all you can. Visit your library and look things up. Ask peers who have had similar issues.

Following are some excellent sources of information:
> An internet search (bookmark websites that you find to be most useful for easy reference)
> Chat groups and list serves
> Public, hospital, medical, and organizational libraries
> Mental health agencies and organizations
> Workshops and seminars
> Mental health newsletters, both online and paper (you can sign up for these online)
> Support groups
> Health care providers
> Pharmacists

CDs and DVDs
People who have similar issues

In doing your search, remember:

It is not safe to share personal information on the computer — if personal information is required to access a site, choose another site.

There is a lot of information on the internet that is not true, is partially true, or that is advertising a particular product. Before deciding you agree with information you find online, check to see where the information came from. Is it from an individual whose background is well known? Is it a national organization that has a good reputation and a philosophy you agree with? Is it sponsored by a company that wants to sell you a product? Is it from a respected hospital or university?

If you are still not sure whether the information is accurate, ask several of your friends and/or a health care provider that you respect.

Once you have gathered the information, study it. Talk to people whose opinions you trust about what you have learned. Pay close attention to how you feel about what you are being told. Don't make any decisions until you feel ready to do so. <u>Make sure what you are doing feels right to you.</u>

Set up an organizational system so that you can easily access information once you have found it, even information that you don't need right now (it may be useful at some other time). This is easy to do on your computer using bookmarks and folders. You can also print or copy articles and information and keep them organized in simple and inexpensive filing systems that you can keep on a shelf, in a drawer, in a milk crate, or even a cardboard box. This is also a good place to keep copies of your test results, and your WRAP, including copies of your Advance Directive.

Keys to Recovery

Self-Advocacy

"It wasn't until I realized that it was up to me, that there was no magic cure, that I began to turn the corner on the road to wellness."

You may feel as if you have lost control over your life, your rights, and your responsibilities, and that you have lost the ability and right to effectively advocate for yourself. You may have very low self-esteem. (See the chapter - "Raising Self-esteem") Regaining your sense of control by successfully advocating for yourself will give you back the hope and self-esteem you need to work toward recovery.

In my studies I have met many remarkable people who spent years completely debilitated by mental health issues and who have learned to be their own best advocate. Many of them are now strong advocates for others with similar issues. Others have leadership and supporting roles in a wide variety of fields.

Tim Field from Seattle, Washington has had mental health challenges for many years. He says, "People need to know and demand their rights in all types of situations from treatment to housing to employment; and they need to know the alternatives available in different situations. Empowerment and recovery start from the inside when you begin to take charge of all aspects of your life. People must always remember that there is hope." Tim is the founder and editor of a Washington State client/consumer mental health newsletter "The Sentinel." He is an excellent example of a person who has found that being a strong advocate for himself and others is essential to feeling in control of his life and getting his depression under control.

Tim goes on to say,

> To me, self-advocacy is part of empowerment, and empowerment is nothing more than learning to take care of yourself every single day, every single hour. Easy to say, but hard to do. For me, empowerment has two parts: involvement and insight.

> Involvement means taking an active role in everything I do or that happens to me, especially when dealing with my mental health problems. Since my depression is a life-threatening problem that continues to periodically rear its head, it is only prudent to learn as much as I can about it, the same as I would if I had cancer or diabetes.

It's not like a broken arm, where I can be passively 'repaired' by a doctor. There is no 'cure' and my life is at stake. That depression is a different kind of problem than a broken arm, in the sense that I can't expect a doctor or therapist to 'fix' me. It took me over 15 years of periodic visits to hell to figure out. So I have set out to learn as much as I can about depression and to integrate this knowledge into knowledge about myself, with a goal of finding what works for me.

I didn't start doing this until I stopped denying what was happening to me. This was the beginning of insight. I believe insight is a way to grow and mature. I decided if I had these problems, I needed to find out what exacerbated them and was bad for me and needed to be avoided. At the same time I needed to learn what is good and truly important to me. It turned out that learning what is good and important is very much a spiritual endeavor for me. Having come so close to death has changed my perspective about many things. Things that many people feel are so important I no longer care about very much: career path, material things, success, wealth, etc. I am letting go of this stuff that used to be so crucial to me. It never did anything but screw me up even worse. Finding what works for me involves exploring new avenues to discover if they have a positive affect on me. In this way I have found powerful positive factors with support groups, new safe friends and places to live and ways of doing things so that I avoid becoming dormant and isolated."

Ten Steps to Being an Effective Self-Advocate

1. Believe in yourself.

You are a unique and valuable person. You are worth the effort it takes to advocate for yourself and protect your rights. You can do it! You may need to work on raising your <u>self-esteem</u> to really believe in yourself and become your own best advocate. (See the chapter "Self-Esteem")

Try repeating over and over again the affirmation, *I am a unique and valuable person. I am worth the effort it takes to advocate for myself and protect my rights.*

____ I already believe in myself. I am going to continue with the work of becoming my own best advocate.

____ I need to work on raising my self-esteem to become my own best advocate. I am going to do this by:

_____

_____

_____

_____

2. **Know your rights.**

You are entitled to equality under the law. Some of us who have had mental health challenges erroneously believe that we do not have the same rights as others. I did for a while. I allowed people I did not know well and did not trust to make decisions for me and take control of my life. I now have systems in place so if I am not able to make good decisions for myself, others of my choice will make them for me.

There are protection and advocacy services in every state. Call them to find out what your rights are. You can get their number by calling your state government information line.

_____ I am committed to learning what my rights are. I will contact my state agency of advocacy and protection to get this information. I will keep a file of my rights in my mental health file.

_____ I have systems in place so if I am not able to make good decisions for myself, others of my choice will make them for me.

_____ I need to put systems in place so if I am not able to make good decisions for myself, others of my choice will make them for me. (See the Crisis Plan that is part of the Wellness Recovery Action Plan.)

3. **Decide what you want.**

Clarify for yourself exactly what you need. This will help you set your own goals and help you be clear to others about what it is that you want and need for yourself.

Your needs may be in the area of treatment. This is often the first area where you gain experience in advocating for yourself. It may have to do with a medication you do, or don't want. It may have to do with whether or not you want electroshock therapy. Perhaps it will be insisting on a complete thyroid examination in the physical examination process (described in the chapter "Medical Considerations"). Maybe it will be asking for a needed sick leave. Perhaps it will be contacting your legislator about health insurance programs that meet your needs.

Your needs might have to do with housing and other services, or education and training.

What do you want or need for yourself?

_____

_____

_____

_____

4. **Get the facts.**

When you advocate for yourself, you need to know what you are talking about or asking for. The internet is an excellent source of information. However, you will need to check its accuracy by looking at several different references to see if they agree. Check with people who have expertise in what you are considering. Ask others who have issues similar to yours. Check references in the library. Contact mental health agencies and organizations for information and support.

As you compile this information, develop a mental health file of hard copies of all pertinent information. Keep it updated and in good order. If you have a computer, keep files on mental health issues there as well. Bookmark sites that you have found to be helpful and reliable.

For instance, when advocating for a complete thyroid test, go to your appointment prepared with appropriate references to show your physician. If advocating for sick leave, contact your state agency of protection and advocacy or your attorney to find out what your rights are.

_____ I have developed mental health files that I keep updated with information as needed.

I need to get the facts about the following issues:

_____

_____

_____

_____

I will get these facts by:

_____

_____

_____

_____

5. **Planning Strategy.**

Using the information you have gathered, plan a strategy that you feel will work to get what you need and want for yourself. Think of several ways to address the problem. Ask supporters for suggestions. Get feedback on your ideas. Then choose to take action using the one that you feel has the most chance of being successful.

Ideas on how to address the issue:

_____

_____

_____

_____

I am going to use the following strategy:

_____

_____

_____

_____

Why did you choose this strategy?

_____

_____

_____

_____

6. **Gather Support.**

In advocating for what you need and want for yourself, it is helpful to have support from family members, friends and other people who have similar issues.

Talk with them about what you are trying to achieve. Ask for their ideas and feedback. You can even ask them to go with you when you are asking for something you need, want, and deserve for yourself. If necessary, call your protection and advocacy organization for additional support.

I am going to ask for support from the following people in working on this issue.

_____

_____

_____

_____

7. **Target efforts.**

Who is the person, persons, or organization you need to deal with to get action on this matter? Talk directly with the person who can best assist you. It may take a few phone calls to discover which organization or person can help, or who is in charge, but it is worth the effort. Keep trying until you find the right person. Maybe the right person is your spouse or another family member. Perhaps it is the head of the local housing agency, your doctor, a case manager, a vocational rehabilitation counselor, or a state legislator.

I am going to contact (names) _____, _____, _____, _____ , and ask them to help me get what it is I want and need for myself.

8. **Express yourself clearly.**

When you are asking for what you need and want for yourself, be brief. Stick to the point. Don't allow yourself to be diverted or to ramble on with unimportant details. State your concern and how you want things changed. If the other person tries to tell you reasons why you cannot achieve what it is you want for yourself, repeat again what it is you want and expect until they either give it to you, help you get it, or refer you to someone else who may be able to give you what you need. If you feel this may be difficult for you, you may want to role-play different scenarios with a supporter or a counselor.

_____ I am going to express myself clearly until I get what it is that I need or until I get more information to help me get what I need.

____ I am going to role-play self-advocacy scenarios with _____, _____, _____.

9. **Assert yourself calmly.**

Don't lose your temper and lash out at the other person, their character or the organization. **Speak out, asking for what you need and want and then listen.** Respect the rights of others, but don't let them "put you down" or "walk all over you."

Repeat these affirmations over and over until they are easy and comfortable for you:

In advocating for myself, I will keep calm because I know this increases my effectiveness.

In advocating for myself, I am committed to speaking out, respecting the rights of others and listening to what they have to say.

In advocating for myself, I will be brief, clear and stick to the point.

I expect people to be respectful of me.

10. **Be firm and persistent.**

Don't give up! Keep after what you want. Always follow through on what you say. Dedicate yourself to getting whatever it is you need for yourself.

Repeat the following affirmation to facilitate this process:

I will be firm and persistent. I will stick with it until I get what I need for myself.

Meeting in person

Speaking to someone in person is the most effective way to advocate for yourself. <u>Make an appointment.</u> Don't just "show up."

Plan what you are going to say and the points you need to make. Practice with the help of friends, recorders, or mirrors if you feel unsure of yourself.

Dress neatly for the appointment. This gives the person the message that this is an important meeting.
<u>Be on time</u>.

Look the person in the eye and shake hands firmly in greeting, unless your culture has different courtesies. Call the person by name. Use positive body language.

How you say something often makes a greater impression than what you say. State your message clearly and simply. Tell the person exactly what it is that you want. Explain why you need it. Tell them why it is in their best interest to respond to your request. Speak loudly enough to be heard without shouting. Expect a positive response.

Listen to what the other person is saying. If you don't understand, ask questions for clarification. If you feel you are not getting anywhere, tell the other person that you wish to pursue your issues further and ask to speak to the person's supervisor.

At the end of the meeting, restate any action that has been decided upon so you both understand each other clearly. For instance, you might say, "As a result of this meeting you are going to order a thyroid test for me." Or, "As a result of this meeting, I understand that you are going to change my status to active." Thank the person for their time and assistance.

Send a follow-up note or e-mail thanking them for meeting with you and summarizing any agreed-upon action. It is a nice gesture. It also acts as a reminder and provides assurance that you both have the same understanding about the result of the meeting.

Sample thank you note:

Dear Ms. Gretsky:

Thank you for meeting with me last Wednesday morning. I appreciate your attention to my housing situation. I look forward to hearing from you next week, after you have contacted Mr. Stiglios.

Very sincerely,

Jane Drew

Getting Action through Letter Writing or Sending an E-mail

Writing is a useful way to request information, present facts, express your opinion, or to ask for what you need for yourself. Make the letter or e-mail short, simple and clear. One page is best. Long letters or e-mails may not be read and it is likely that they don't stick to the point.

A bulleted list of key points is a good strategy.

It is acceptable to write the letter by hand if you don't have access to a typewriter or computer, but make sure it is readable and legible. You may think it is readable and legible, but you are used to your own style of writing and already know what you are trying to say. Ask a supporter if your handwritten letter is clearly readable, understandable, and legible to them. Computer word processing services are inexpensive and might be worth the cost.

If appropriate, send copies of your letter or e-mail to others you want informed, such as your legislator or advocacy agency. Put "cc" (which means copies circulated) at the bottom of the letter with a list of others to whom you are sending copies. For e-mails, put the e-mail addresses of others you are sending copies to in the "cc" line in your mail program. If you don't want to share other people's e-mail addresses, put them in the "bcc" (blind copy) line of your e-mail message.

Keep a copy of the letter or e-mail in a special file for future reference. Follow up a letter with a phone call to make sure the person got the letter or e-mail and to discuss the situation further.

Advocating for Yourself by Phone

Letters, e-mails and visits may be initiated or followed with phone calls if appropriate. The telephone is useful to gather information, to keep track of what's going on, and to let people know what you want. Before you call, make a list of the essential points you want to cover that you can refer to so you don't forget anything.

When calling;

1. Identify yourself. Ask who you are speaking to and their position (Who am I speaking to? What is your position?).

2. Briefly describe the situation to the person who answered and ask if they are the right person to deal with such a request. If they are not the right person, ask to be transferred to a person who is more appropriate. If that person is not available, leave them a voicemail message asking them to return your call. If you have not heard from them by the next day, call back. Keep calling until you reach the person you need to speak to.

3. Once you have reached the appropriate person, make your request for action brief and clear.

4. If the person cannot respond to your request immediately, ask when they will get back to you or by what date you can expect action.

5. Thank the person for being helpful when that's the case.

6. In some cases when a person has been particularly helpful, it is a good idea to send a note or e-mail of thanks. This opens the door for further contact on related issues.

7. Keep a written record of your calls in your file. Include the date of your call, the name of the person you talked with, issues addressed and promised action. Computer calendars with a reminder system are a good way to keep track of when you were in touch and when you might need to be in touch again.

8. If you do not hear back from the person when expected, if the promised action is not taken or the situation is not resolved, call them back. Persist until you reach them, the promised action is taken or resolution is reached.

Learning Communication Skills

Protection and advocacy services, local and statewide mental health organizations, the internet and the public library are good sources of information on self-advocacy, assertiveness, and effective communication. Take advantage of classes that may be available through community colleges or adult education programs.

Making Arrangements for Times When You Can't Make Decisions for Yourself

Everyone hopes that each difficult time will be their last. Even with your best intentions and efforts, this may not be the case. While hard times may get less frequent or lessen in intensity as you learn how to better manage them, they may continue to be an issue. Use the window of opportunity when you are doing well to develop a Crisis Plan or Advance Directive *(see Appendix)* that describes the care you want for yourself if you get into a situation where you cannot make good decisions for yourself. If you have not prepared in advance for difficult times, decisions made on your behalf may not be decisions you would make for yourself if you were able to do so.

Before developing a Crisis Plan or an Advance Directive, carefully research all treatment options. You can get information from your physician, counselor, mental health organizations and the internet so that you can make good decisions about what you want for yourself. Include in your study information that expresses a variety of viewpoints.

Everyone is different. We have different physiologies, different responses to treatments, different tolerance levels, and different feelings about the use of specific treatments. You have a right to have these differences respected. Therefore, everyone's Advance Directive or Crisis Plan will be different.

Laws about Advance Directives and Crisis Plans and their legality differ from state to state. Check with your attorney or state office of protection and advocacy to see what kind of a document is legal in your state. Even if these documents are not legal in your state, they will be a helpful guide to your chosen supporters.

Store copies of your Advance Directive or Crisis Plan in your health file or on your computer. Give copies to each of the people listed and to your attorney. Discuss the documents with them to be sure everyone is clear about your intent.

Hospitalization Rights

The rights of a person who is hospitalized, especially a person who is hospitalized against his or her will (this generally only happens if a person is a danger to themselves or others), varies from state to state. You may feel that you have been neglected, harshly treated or inappropriately treated in a hospital. You might also feel that you have not received the same quality of care as people with similar kinds of issues. Contact your state office of protection and advocacy if you have concerns about how you have been, or are being treated. If you cannot do this yourself, ask a supporter to do it for you.

Here is a general list of what you have a right to expect in any health care facility. Give copies of this list to supporters so they can advocate for you if you cannot advocate for yourself.

Personal Rights

1. I have the right to communicate in person, by sending and receiving mail and e-mail, and by having reasonable access to telephones and computers, with the people of my choice.

2. I have the right to wear my own clothing.

3. I have the right to keep my personal possessions, including safe toilet articles.

4. I have the right to my personal beliefs.

5. I have the right to a private, safe storage area for my things, to which I have free access.

6. I have the right to privacy to perform personal hygiene tasks.

7. I have the right to work with my care providers to develop a written treatment plan that we update as my condition or treatment changes.

8. I have the right to refuse any potentially unusual or hazardous treatment procedures medication or treatment.

9. I have the right to be represented by counsel whenever my rights may be affected.

10. I have the right to not be required to perform routine labor tasks of the facility except those essential for treatment.

11. I have the right to the same civil rights as a person not in a such a facility.

12. I have the right to be treated with respect, dignity and compassion, and in the same manner and with the same effects, and in the same manner and with the same effects as a person not in such a facility.

Keys to Recovery

Support

My support team is absolutely crucial to my wellness. I maintain good relationships with supporters through honest communication – trying not to "burden" any one supporter too much.

A structured support system of people with whom you have ongoing contact is essential if you are working on your recovery. While others can have a more casual approach to developing and keeping a strong support system, that does not work if you have mental health challenges. Develop a support plan and stick to it to be assured that you always have the support that is so essential to wellness. While your recovery journey is yours alone, you need others to pave the way, monitor the passage, enrich your existence, and counter feelings of loneliness and isolation.

The following quotes are from people I interviewed:

"My support team is absolutely essential to my long term wellness. I never really think about 'giving up' anymore. They are always willing to listen – to both my joys and my sorrows. I maintain close relationships with them through regular phone calls."

"My support team is extremely important to my ongoing wellness. I keep good relationships with them by keeping appointments, being in touch, being honest, and not taking on more than I can handle."

Everyone could benefit from at least five good friends or supporters we can call on when we need support, people who can count on us when they need a friend as well. This chapter describes how you can build, strengthen, and use a support system. You may not have five supporters when you begin to work on this. Gradually, through using the strategies described, the number of your supporters and their role in enhancing your wellness will increase.

How many supporters can you identify now? Include family members, friends, and health care providers. _____
Who are they?

_____

_____

_____

_____

_____

What do you want from supporters and what do you give to your supporters?

Supporters listen to you and let you express your feelings and emotions without judging or criticizing. Many people are not used to listening without making some comment about the content. They feel that if you are saying something, they need to tell you if you are right or wrong and what you should do about it. This doesn't help. Tell your supporters that if you want their advice and feedback, you will ask for it. Otherwise you just want them to listen.

At the beginning of the time you plan to spend together, let the supporter know what you want. For instance, you might say, "Today I just need you to listen to me while I express my feelings and figure out this situation for myself." Another time you might say, "I'd like some feedback and advice." Being clear is the best way to get what you need and want for yourself.

In return, spend as much time listening to your supporters as they spend listening to you. Using the exchange listening structure (see the chapter "Exchange Listening") is a good way to insure that you both get equal time to be heard. Do for them what they do for you, letting them freely express their feelings and emotions without being judged or criticized, and providing advice and feedback only when requested.

If you have had years of dealing with mental health challenges along with loss and rejection, you may find it difficult to understand that another person likes you, accepts you and wants to spend time with you. To increase your ability to understand that people like you, try the following exercises:

- Ask the other person to tell you five things they like about you, then you tell them five things you like about them. Do this often!

- Ask the other person to spend five minutes (use a timer) telling you why they like you, then do the same for them. You can both repeat the same things over and over, for example – "You are a warm, friendly, and interesting person." Repeat this exercise often!

- Develop a positive rebuttal to the negative thought, "*No one likes me.*" Change it to, "*Many people like me.*" Repeat over and over to yourself or to your supporter, "Many people like me." Repeat it when you are stuck in traffic, when you are washing the dishes, when you are waiting in the doctor's office, before you fall asleep at night, whenever you have empty time to fill. Take a moment to focus on what it feels like in your body to know that people like you. Before long you will truly know that many people like you.

• Make a list of people who like you. Make copies. Then hang them in prominent places around your house to act as constant reminders. Add names to the list as new people come into your life.

Spend most of your time with supporters doing fun, interesting activities together, not just dealing with emotions and heavy issues. Often you meet supporters through shared interests. As the relationship proceeds, don't forget to do those things that you enjoyed doing together when you first met. You can suggest and initiate activities sometimes and your supporters can suggest and initiate activities sometimes.

Make a list of the things you like to do together. Then you have it available when you are trying to think of something to do together.

The things I like to do with _____ are:

_____

_____

_____

_____

_____

The things I like to do with _____ are:

_____

_____

_____

_____

_____

Your supporters allow you the space to change, grow, make decisions, and even mistakes. They allow and encourage you to express your feelings and emotions, and your needs and wants. Don't expect them to have you all figured out or have all the answers for you.

Your supporters share information with you that they think would be valuable to you, such as an article on light therapy, a helpful website or a webinar that might help you with your WRAP. You share similar information with them.

Your supporters have taken the time to educate themselves about mental health challenges like you experience. They have read books, attended workshops and seminars, and even in some cases, accompanied you on visits to health care providers. You have educated yourself about issues that are important to your supporters as well. For instance, if a supporter is diabetic, you can learn about that disorder.

Supporters work with you to decide the next best step to take in a difficult situation, when you ask them for that help. Then, when you have figured out what to do next, they do whatever they can to assist you in taking that step!

Your supporters provide encouragement when you need it. You encourage them when they need it as well. One person said, "I appreciate my friends and family encouraging me when I decide to get medical help for depression. I have asked those close to me to encourage me to get help when I am 'stuck' and not functioning."

When you can't make decisions, take action on your own behalf, and advocate for yourself, your supporters can do this for you. They refer to your Crisis Plan or Advance Directive (see chapters on Developing a Wellness Recovery Action Plan) in order to determine actions to take on your behalf. Give your supporters copies of these documents as soon as you have them completed. Give them updated copies whenever you revise these plans. They may ask you to do this for them when they are in a situation where they need you to help them make decisions, take action on their behalf and advocate for them when they can't do this for themselves.

Who can be your supporters?

Your supporters are people you like, respect, trust, with whom you share common interests and rapport, and with whom you can share <u>anything</u>. You choose them yourself. No one else can determine who should be your supporter. These are very individual, personal choices. You do not need to justify your choices to anyone. Your supporters can be family members, peers, friends, co-workers and health care providers. However, health care providers may be limited in the kind of support they can offer.

You may want to ask someone who already fits in the category of a supporter to help you figure out who may be other possible supporters for you and where you might meet them. But the choice is always yours. I am going to discuss possible supporters with _____
_____.

Where you can meet supporters

Support Groups Support groups are wonderful places to make new, understanding friends. They may be groups for people who have mental health challenges. Or they could be support groups that deal with a variety of other issues, like weight management, parenting issues, and issues related to sexuality. People reported that this is where they formed long-lasting friendships and some even found appropriate partners. Support groups counter the social isolation which many people experience.

Support groups provide an opportunity to be with people who have similar problems and issues, people who understand and can be supportive. They help you to feel you are not alone. Communication is easy. Groups members help you to appreciate your own circumstances, that things are not as bleak as they seemed, that there is hope, and that others with similar issues are doing very well.

There are numerous support groups available. They are generally listed in the community calendar section of the newspaper. Mental health agencies and organizations also can refer you to support groups. Attend a support group several times before making a decision about whether it is the right one for you. Every group can have an off night where things just don't "gel."

You may want to start your own support group. Get together with several friends, ask them to come to a meeting, and encourage them to invite other friends as well. The group could meet as often as the members choose and the group could decide its focus, or if it even wants a focus. Often such groups are strictly social and simply provide an opportunity to get out and be with people who can be counted on to be understanding and supportive.

Quotes from people about their experiences with support groups:

"I am in a support group of about fifteen people. In the group, people talk about how they are managing their lives. If they request it, they can receive feedback from others in the group. It is very helpful. You can see others who have similar issues who see things from a slightly different perspective. Also the supportive atmosphere helps a lot."

"The support group helps me to know that I am not alone with these issues, to get along better with others, understanding people, and listening to others and having others listen to me."

"The support group rules insist on confidentiality, no vulgarity, are nonconfrontational, and no one can monopolize the conversation. Although there are sometimes educational programs, the most important thing is SHARING. It has taught me not to get too involved in other people's problems. If they ask for help I suggest something. If they don't follow my advice, I have no problem. I am not one to say I told you so."

"We treat each other as equals. We talk and listen to each other. We go on some outings together. We meet once a week. It is very helpful to me, providing me with a social life."

_____ I already belong to a support group.

Describe how it has been helpful. _____

_____

Have you met people at the support group who are now your supporters? ___
If so, who are they?

_____

_____

_____ I am going to locate and join a support group.

_____ I am going to locate a group by _____

_____

Volunteer. There are many agencies that could use your help. Inquire at places like churches, schools, hospitals, youth agencies, soup kitchens, and the Red Cross office. Many communities have organizations which coordinate volunteers and would be a good resource when you are looking for just the right place to volunteer.

When you are volunteering, you have the opportunity to meet others with common interests while doing something you enjoy. Regular contact encourages the development of supportive relationships. When you meet someone you particularly enjoy, invite them to share an activity. Encourage ongoing contact through phone calls and get togethers.

_____ I am a volunteer.

Describe how this has been useful to you. _____

_____

People I met through volunteering who are now my supporters: _____

_____

____ I am going to volunteer.

____ I am going to locate a volunteer position by: _____

_____

_____

Community Activities and Special Interest Groups Many communities offer a broad range of activities, special interest and action groups. These may be open to the public or accessible by becoming member. Use your local newspaper as a guide to finding these groups. Attend those activities and events that interest you. Like others, you may look through the newspaper and say to yourself, "that would be fun" or "that would be interesting." Then you don't follow through and attend. Set yourself a goal of attending one or several community activities on a regular basis. When you see the same person several times, start a conversation. If they seem interesting, invite them to an activity or to stop for a snack on the way home. If you enjoy each other, continue the relationship by making a plan for another time to get together each time you reconnect. These activities not only bring us new supporters, they enrich our lives.

___ I already go to community activities and events that interest me.

Describe how has this been useful to you. _____

_____

_____

People I have met at these events who are now my supporters:_____

_____

_____

____ I am going to start attending community events on regular basis.

____ I am going to locate such events by: _____

_____

_____

Areas of interests include: _____

_____

Take a class. Isn't there something you'd like to learn? Take a class in another language, computer science, bird watching, knitting, wood carving, literature, pottery – whatever interests you. Many of them are inexpensive. Scholarship aid may be available. The classroom situation and the shared interest make it an excellent place to meet new people. In addition, they are a wonderful place to explore career options. Choices are listed in newspapers and on the internet. Look up the websites of local schools, educational facilities, and organizations for ideas.

___ I already take classes that interest me.

Describe how this has been useful to you in building support. _____
_____
_____

People I met at classes who are now my supporters: _____
_____
_____

____ I am going to start attending a class.

____ I am going to locate classes by: _____
_____
_____

Areas of interest include _____
_____
_____

Keep in touch with friends and acquaintances. Many people lose touch with others they enjoy because they don't keep in touch. When you meet someone you like, invite them out for coffee, lunch, or to share an activity. When you are parting, make a plan for the next time to get together. I have several close friends with whom I have a set time every week when I get together with them for an hour. Schedule contact with people you like.

Can you think of anyone right now with whom you would like to renew contact? _____ If so, who?
_____

Describe how you could reconnect with this person. _____
_____
_____

Making the Connection

When you feel you have identified a person who meets all your criteria for a supporter:
- Ask them if they are willing to be your supporter. (Explain to them what that means, what you want and need from your supporters.)

- Tell them that, in return, you will be their supporter, providing for them all the same things that you expect of them. (It needs to be clear this is a two-way, not a one-way relationship, you are requesting.)

- Tell them you have several supporters and that it is not necessary that they be available at all times. (If you call and ask for company or assistance and they are not available, they should tell you and you will contact another person on your list. At any given time your supporter may have reasons why they are unavailable, including work responsibilities, family responsibilities, other plans, illness, or a vacation. It is very important that if a person says they are unavailable, you respect that and find another person to meet your needs. This keeps them from getting "burned out" and keeps you from interfering with their life.)

For instance, I asked my friend Bev to be a supporter. I told her that meant that I could call her if I needed support and assistance, and that we would keep in contact on a regular basis, either through a phone call or an activity. I explained that what I wanted most was someone to share activities (something we were already doing), and someone to listen. I explained that she was one of several people I was asking to be my supporter. I told her that there might be times when I would ask for feedback and advice and maybe times when she would be needed to consult with other supporters and take action on my behalf when I couldn't do that for myself. In addition, I explained to her that this meant that I would also provide her with the same kind of support. Bev agreed and we became supporters.

If you feel uncomfortable asking someone to be your supporter, practice asking for support by role-playing with your counselor, a peer, family member, friend, or supporter.

_____ I feel uncomfortable asking someone to be my supporter.

_____ I am going to practice by role-playing with _____

Managing relationships with supporters. Spend lots of quality time with your supporters, sharing activities that you both enjoy – perhaps just sitting around talking, listening to music, playing musical instruments, cooking a meal and eating it, woodworking, going for a walk – anything you both enjoy doing together. Your work, family responsibilities, other activities, and those of your supporter, determine how much time you can spend together.

_____ I am committed to spending quality time with my supporters.

Keep regular contact with members of your support team, even when things are going well. Have a commitment to keep weekly contact with members of your support team. You all have busy schedules. Just a phone call will suffice sometimes.

_____ I am committed to having at least one contact with each member of my support team every week.

Spend time listening and supporting each other. Many people have found it useful to set this contact up on a regular basis. For instance, every Friday afternoon from one to two, I meet with my friend Laura for an exchange listening session. Have an appointment book or keep an up-to-date calendar on your computer to keep track of these times.

_____ I am going to set up regular contact with the following supporters.

Who? _____ How often? (weekly, every other week, monthly, etc.)

_____

Who? _____ How often? _____

Who? _____ How often? _____

You may want to include contact with your supporters as a Wellness Tool in your WRAP® Wellness Toolbox. Then you can include it in the various action plans that are part of your WRAP®.

Why you may have a hard time setting up a support system. You may have felt you don't deserve to be supported. Many people feel that way. It may be more of an issue for people with mental health challenges, if you felt you had not reached your goals, lived up to your potential, or lived up to the expectations others had for you. You may have been told by people you care about, and health care providers, that you will never amount to anything and that you will always have mental health difficulties. You may have been made to feel that you do not have as much value as others. You may tend to minimize the value of your accomplishments and achievements.

You may feel unloved and unlovable. This might keep you from reaching out for the support, attention, respect and love you deserve. You may feel no one would want to give these things to someone as unworthy as you are. You may be afraid you will be rejected, and that will hurt more than if you had never reached out.

The truth is you have just as much value as anyone else. You deserve support, attention, respect, and love. If you reach out to find people in the right places and give them the same kind of support, attention, respect and love they give you, you will find that you have many strong supporters.

Repeat over and over to yourself, whenever you have an opportunity: *I am a lovable person and I deserve support, attention, respect, and love.* Before long you will know that this affirmation is true. Knowing that you are lovable and deserve support, attention, respect, and love will facilitate the process of setting up your support team.

People who have mental health challenges can be needy and draining. You may have become dependent on one or two people to meet your needs and didn't realize that you needed to be supportive of those people when you were able. They may have quickly tired, and quietly, or sometimes loudly, disappeared from your life. Avoid this difficult situation by:

1. having many close supporters so you don't wear anyone out.

2. giving them the same kind of support, attention, respect, and love they give you, making sure the relationship is about 50/50.

3. doing everything you can to take good care of yourself, including developing and using a Wellness Recovery Action Plan (WRAP®).

Inappropriate social skills embarrass and turn off others. Because of your mental health challenges, you may never have had an opportunity to learn social skills that are generally accepted in society. Inappropriate social skills include things like:

- talking incessantly without giving anyone else a chance to talk
- not paying attention when others are talking
- being very demanding
- not being sensitive to the needs of others
- being inappropriately loud and boisterous in public places
- being inappropriately physically affectionate
- interrupting when others are talking

- excessively borrowing things from people, like cigarettes
- not practicing good personal hygiene
- excessive use of profanity

Ask your peers, health care providers, and others you respect and trust if you have any social habits or skills that others may find offensive. Listen to what they have to say without getting angry or being defensive. Ask others to verify these opinions. Then work with your peers, family members, and health care providers to change these habits. Admitting to others that you are working on eliminating these habits may be difficult, but it helps. It will take some work. You will need to be supported while you do it.

I feel that I have the following inappropriate social skills:

_____

_____

_____

_____

_____

_____

I am going to work with _____ to change these habits to more appropriate ones.

Keys to Keeping a Strong Support System

Once you have built a strong support system, how are you going to keep it strong?

1. Do everything you can to keep yourself well and stable. Make your wellness your highest priority. Develop and use a Wellness Recovery Action Plan (WRAP®).

2. Work on development of appropriate social skills if this is an issue for you. This can be effectively accomplished in working with peers, health care providers, counseling, and exchange listening sessions.

3. Be an active member of a support group.

4. Be mutually supportive. This means being there for others when they need you, as well as asking them to be there for you when you need them.

8. Have several friends so you don't drain any one. Paying attention to their needs is important for both of you.

9. Educate your supporters about your issues so they will know what to expect and how to deal with problems if they come up.

10. Give supporters copies of your Crisis Plan or Advance Directive so they will know how to support you if you cannot take care of yourself.

11. Arrange meetings between your key supporters and health care providers when you are well, so that if they need to contact each other when you are having a hard time, they will already be acquainted. Let supporters know who your health care providers are, what role they play, and how they can be contacted. This facilitates the process of getting you help.

_____ I am going to arrange meetings between my support team and my health care providers.

12. Many people have had meetings of their support team. At these meetings you explain what you want from your supporters, signs that indicate you are having a hard time and need help, actions you want supporters to take on your behalf when needed. This is a good time for members of your support team to get each other's phone numbers and the phone numbers of health care providers so they can coordinate efforts if necessary. These meetings also provide an opportunity to educate support team members about what you experience or might experience. Some people choose to have one meeting. Others feel more comfortable with ongoing meetings, perhaps once a month or every two or three months. One person said :

"I meet once a week with my supporters. I know I can talk about anything with them and they aren't going to make fun of me or think I am losing it all! The best way to maintain these relationships is by being myself and being supportive to them."

Potluck suppers are great. The work is shared and there's always a good variety of tasty food. A friend whose family is less accessible found it helpful to have a series of potluck suppers at her home. She said only part of the time was spent on discussing issues related to her wellness. The rest of the time they socialized.

_____ I am going to set up a meeting of my supporters.

When _____ Where _____

13. Exchange listen with your supporters. Set up a regular time to get together for a specific time – for example at 2:00 every Tuesday afternoon. Divide the time in half. The first half of the time one person gets to talk, share, cry, whatever, with the full attention of the other person. The second half of the time, the roles are reversed. This method tends to deepen relationships, helps people to feel better about themselves, and often, using this method, we can sort out the answers to pressing problems. Exchange listening is discussed fully in the chapter "Exchange Listening."

_____ I already do exchange listening.
How has it helped you keep your support system strong?

_____
_____

_____ I am going to try exchange listening.
When? _____ With whom? _____

_____ I don't want to try exchange listening. If not, why not?

_____
_____

14. Make a list of your support team members with phone numbers. Many of us have a goal of having at least five people on our support team. Others have more. As you implement the strategies above and have new supporters, update your list. When we most need to reach out to our supporters is the time when it is hardest to remember who they are. Have copies of the list by your phones, on your bedside table and in your purse or pocket.

Support Team Members

Name	Phone Number
1. _____	_____
2. _____	_____
3. _____	_____
4. _____	_____
5. _____	_____

Name	**Phone Number**

6. _____

7. _____

8. _____

9. _____

10. _____

11. _____

12. _____

WRAP®

Introduction to WRAP®

By far, the most exciting thing that has happened in my work, and I feel, in the entire mental health field, is the development of a simple and safe self-help strategy and guide to daily living and recovery – the Wellness Recovery Action Plan, commonly known as WRAP®.

In the winter of 1997, I was leading a recovery seminar in northern Vermont. It was one day a week for eight full days. In that time, I shared with people the key concepts of recovery and we discussed at length the many recovery strategies that I had discovered through my ongoing interviews with people who have a lived experience of mental health difficulties. The weather was as harsh as it can be in a northern Vermont winter, and I was pleasantly surprised when I arrived each week, often after a harrowing trip on icy roads, to find 30-45 people waiting to begin our work together.

At the last session, I was beginning to pat myself on the back for a job well-done, when a woman stood up in the back of the room and said, "This is all well and good, but I have been in and out of mental institutions all across the country, and I wouldn't have any idea how to organize what you have taught into my life." What a challenge!

The state had allowed us extra days together to follow up on our work. As I was traveling to the first of these follow-up days with Jane Winterling, she suggested we set up a system so that people could keep track of how they are doing and particular responses for when they weren't doing so well. I took that idea to the group. Over the next days that we had together we worked and worked and worked. And our final product was WRAP®. It included:

A listing of Wellness Tools
Daily Maintenance Plan
    What I am like when I am well
    What I need to do every day to stay as well as possible
    What I might need to do on any given day to stay as well as possible
Triggers
    Identification
    Action Plan
Early Warning Signs
    Identification
    Action Plan

When Things are Breaking Down
      Identification
      Action Plan
  Crisis Plan or Advance Directive

The Post Crisis Plan was added several years later at the suggestion of Richard Hart, who felt that this addition would complete the recovery circle.

When I got home that afternoon, a gray, snowy day in March, I developed my first personal WRAP and began using it as a guide to my everyday life. I had been doing fairly well over time, but this was a huge boost in my recovery. I noticed right away that I was more aware of how I was feeling, and how I was doing, and was able to take steps to help myself feel and do better more quickly. I saw changes in every part of my life, my work life, my relationships, my family, my leisure times, and my support circle. I was thrilled.

A couple of months later, I was developing a workshop to present at a major international mental health conference. I decided to take a risk and teach WRAP. I had no idea how it would be received. It was a bit scary. When I got there, I noticed on the program that there were lots of workshops on medications and invasive treatments, and workshops on the brain structure, but nothing at all on what a person could do to help her/ or himself. I was afraid I might get booed out of the hall. As the hall began to fill with eager participants, I became more and more skeptical. How would I be received? Should I just go back to my usual format, or take this risk?

I took the risk. I gave the first WRAP presentation. People were hesitant at first, but after they got the idea of what was happening, they began to participate, calling out their own responses and suggestions. At the end, a woman in the back stood up and said, "Finally, something we can do to help ourselves." It was then that I knew that WRAP was off and running. But I could never have imagined where it would go.

Now, 13 years later, WRAP is an evidence-based practice. You can learn more about the research findings at the website http://mentalhealthrecovery.com/wrap_program_desc.php#. I have traveled all over the world teaching WRAP and teaching people how to facilitate WRAP groups. I have written numerous books and developed a widely used curriculum and various resources, including CDs, DVDs, and online learning programs that teach WRAP and the other recovery skills and strategies that I have learned through my research. Thousands of people are trained to facilitate WRAP groups. Hundreds of agencies and organizations across the globe use WRAP as the cornerstone of their mental health recovery programs. And hundreds of thousands of people (based on resource sales and workshop attendance figures) are using WRAP as their guide to daily living, recovery and wellness.

The Copeland Center for Wellness and Recovery was developed in 2004 to insure the continued spread of WRAP into the future. It is now responsible for trainings and educational outreach based on my studies, including, of course, WRAP.

Over time, it became clear that WRAP was different from other kinds of recovery planning — that a WRAP is only a WRAP if a person develops it for him/ or herself. No one else can develop a WRAP for anyone else. No one else can be responsible for another person's WRAP. Others can give ideas. But the final WRAP is developed by, and belongs to, the individual whose life it will guide. WRAP cannot be mandated. It is totally voluntary. This was quite different from plans that were often developed by case managers or counselors, and then signed by the person who was supposed to follow it.

Although anyone can develop a WRAP on their own, many, many people found that working with others in small groups helped them develop a personal WRAP that worked well for them. Guidance from a trained facilitator and lots and lots of ideas from others with lived experience made WRAP work for people. That is why I trained so many WRAP facilitators, why we developed the Copeland Center to continue these trainings and why there is a huge network of WRAP facilitators spreading the word about WRAP.

As people worked with WRAP, values and ethics grew up around WRAP. People everywhere agreed that these values and ethics were essential to the success of this innovation.

WRAP Values and Ethics

1. WRAP supports the premise that there is hope, that people can get well, stay well for long periods of time, and do the things they want to do with their lives.

2. Self-determination, personal responsibility, empowerment, and self-advocacy are key to WRAP.

3. WRAP programs include group decision-making about group process and personal sharing.

4. All participants in WRAP programs are treated as equals with dignity, compassion, mutual respect, and unconditional high regard.

5. In WRAP programs there is unconditional acceptance of each person as they are – unique, special individuals, including acceptance of diversity with relation to culture, ethnicity, language, religion, race, gender, age, disability, sexual identity, and "readiness" issues.

6. The WRAP program is based on the premise that there are "no limits" to recovery.

7. In developing a WRAP, it is understood that each person is the expert on her or himself.

8. The focus of WRAP is on individual strengths and away from perceived deficits.

9. Clinical, medical and diagnostic language is not part of WRAP and is avoided in WRAP programs.

10. The focus of WRAP groups is on peers working together and learning from each other to increase mutual understanding and knowledge, and to promote wellness.

11. WRAP emphasizes strategies that are simple and safe for anyone and de-emphasizes strategies that may have harmful effects.

12. In WRAP groups and WRAP work, difficult feelings and behaviors are seen as normal responses to traumatic circumstances and in the context of what is happening and not as symptoms or a diagnosis.

The next three chapters describe the WRAP process.

WRAP®

Wellness Toolbox

Let's get started on your WRAP®. The first thing you need to do is develop your Wellness Toolbox. The Wellness Toolbox is the cornerstone of WRAP®. It is an ever-expanding list of tools – actions, activities and behaviors – that you can use to develop the actions plans that are part of each section of WRAP®. These tools will also give you lots of ideas of things to do whenever you are trying to decide what to do. You may start with a very short list. But over time you will notice more and more Wellness Tools to add to your list.

The best way to develop your list of Wellness Tools is working with a group. People in the group get so many ideas from each other. Working with a group in Oklahoma, my spouse and I developed a list of over 80 top-notch wellness tools. If you want to work on your WRAP® with a group, call your local mental health agencies or organizations to find out if there are any WRAP® groups in your area that you could attend, or see if there is a group listed in your area on the website www.wraparoundtheworld.com. You can also take the "Build Your Own WRAP®" program, and "Creating a Wellness Toolbox" online learning courses at www.mentalhealthrecovery.com and use the various WRAP® resource books, especially Winning Against Relapse, to assist you in developing your Wellness Toolbox.

Many people develop their WRAP® in a three ring binder. They write their lists of Wellness Tools on sheets of binder paper, inserted in the front of the binder for easy reference when they are developing their WRAP®, and for daily use. If you are using the **Build Your Own WRAP program** (www.mentalhealthrecovery.com), you can store your Wellness Tool list on line and e-mail copies to yourself for your records, and for posting around your home (I have mine on my refrigerator door).

Common Wellness Tools

A key question I always ask myself when I am trying to increase my Wellness Tools is, "What helps me feel better?" Some of the ideas that come quickly to mind are:

    Brushing my teeth
    Taking a shower
    Wearing something I like
    Going to bed by 11 PM
    Fixing my hair

Spending time with my spouse or children
Petting the dog
Working outside in my garden
Walking in the woods
Getting together with a close friend
Bird watching
Connecting with friends on Facebook

Keys to Recovery Wellness Tools

There are questions that you can ask yourself to help you uncover more Wellness Tools. I like to use the Keys to Recovery — hope, personal responsibility, education, self-advocacy, and support — to focus my thoughts about possible Wellness Tools. These Keys to Recovery came out of my early research, have stood the test of time, and are described in the first section of this book.

For instance, Wellness Tools that have to do with HOPE might include:
Reminding yourself of things that give you a feeling of hope like nature, good friends, and helpful care providers
Reading recovery stories
Writing about your goals and dreams
Repeating hopeful affirmations over and over
"Every day in every way I feel better and better."
"People like me get well, stay well, and do the things they want to with their lives."

Wellness Tools that have to do with PERSONAL RESPONSIBILITY might include:
Trying something new
Doing something for yourself that others have done for you in the past
Taking an action that supports your recovery
Making a decision about something you want and need

Wellness Tools that have to do with EDUCATION might include:
Researching medications on the internet
Attending workshops and seminars
Reviewing mental health newsletters
Developing a personal library of resources that support your recovery
Studying a diagnosis or proposed treatment at the library

Wellness tools that have to do with SELF-ADVOCACY might include:

Asking for what you want and need, over and over until you get it

Asking others to support you in advocating for yourself

Knowing your rights and doing what you need to do to assure that they are honored

Reaching out to protection and advocacy agencies for help and support

Wellness Tools that have to do with SUPPORT might include:

Calling a friend

Going to a support group meeting

Asking a friend over for lunch

Exchange listening (described in this book)

Having a potluck supper with a few friends

Treating a friend to a movie

Time listening to family members

Connecting with a friend on Facebook

Chatting with a friend on Facebook

Joining an on-line recovery support group

You can think of many more Wellness Tools that have to do with the Keys to Recovery that you can add to your list.

Creative Activities Wellness Tools

Think about creative activities you enjoy, or would like to try, and add them to your list of Wellness Tools. Some ideas include:

Painting

Collage

Needlework

Woodcraft

Carving

Quilting

Making music

Cooking

Tasks that May be Wellness Tools

What are some tasks that make you feel better when you have done them that might be considered Wellness Tools? They might include:

> Washing the dishes
> Organizing a drawer
> Redecorating a small space in my home
> Rearranging the furniture
> Clearing off my desk
> Weeding my garden
> Polishing my bike
> Dusting
> Clearing out clutter
> Putting a clean table cloth on the table
> Changing the sheets
> Going to the thrift store
> Buying myself something I need

Stress Reduction Wellness Tools

What do you do to relax and reduce the stress in your life? These are things that can be included on your list of Wellness Tools. They might include:

> Meditation
> A Progressive Relaxation Exercise
> 15 minutes of quiet time
> Sitting in the park
> Listening to soothing music
> Watching a funny movie
> Journaling

How do you deal with troubling thoughts, feelings and behaviors when they intrude into your life? These are great times for Wellness Tools. They might include:

> Changing negative thoughts to positive exercises
> Uncovering and analyzing negative thoughts
> Reinforcing positive statements
> Visualizations
> Positive affirmations
> Diverting your attention

Community Resources as Wellness Tools

To continue to build your list of Wellness Tools, you could consider the resources that are available in your community, things like:

Inpatient and outpatient care
Community and senior centers
Crisis respite centers
Alternative care providers
Counseling, consulting, coaching
Special interest groups
Support groups
Educational courses
Community events (concerts, movies, plays)
Stores you like to shop in
Book stores
Second hand stores, antique shops
Lunch shops, pizza parlors, restaurants
Recreation centers
Parks

There are free or low cost services that could be included on your list of wellness tools, things like:

Libraries
Legal aid
Food banks and cooperatives
Meals on wheels programs
Transportation services
Beautician and massage schools

Health-Related Wellness Tools

There are specific Wellness Tools that might be related to your dietary needs, things like:

Eating three healthy meals a day
Eating at least five servings of vegetables a day
Drinking six 8-ounce glasses of water a day
Avoiding excessive sugar, caffeine, high fat and highly salted foods
Eating small healthy snacks between meals
Avoiding overeating

You may have food allergies and preferences that could be part of your list. For instance, I talked to a person who said that whenever she is having a really bad time, it helps her to eat macaroni and cheese. Another person said, "when I eat things that contain wheat, I get all stuffy and feel groggy."

Perhaps you can think of some Wellness Tools that have to do with exercise. Some ideas include:

Spending ten minutes a day doing stretching exercise

Going for a twenty-minute walk 3-5 times a week

Climbing the stairs twice every day

Dancing, biking, swimming, running, strolling

Playing basketball

Golf or miniature golf

Many people find that getting exposure to outside light each day helps them to feel better. Wellness Tools that have to do with getting exposure to outside light might include:

Spending at least one half hour each day outside

When inside, spend time in well-lighted spaces and near windows

Exposing myself to supplemental full spectrum light each morning for half an hour

Putting the window shades up every day

Sitting outside on a bench while I am having lunch

You may discover that you have some Wellness Tools that have to do with sleep. Some of the common ones that others have reported include:

Going to bed at 11 o'clock every night

Getting up at 7 o'clock every morning

Avoiding caffeine, alcohol and nicotine

Engaging in quiet activities for at least a half hour before going to bed

Having a turkey sandwich and a glass of milk before going to bed

Avoiding using my computer in the evening

If you are a smoker, you may have Wellness Tools that have to do with smoking. They might include:

Limiting smoking each day to five cigarettes

Avoiding places where people are smoking

Gradually cutting back on smoking by one cigarette a day

Avoiding smoking

Reminding myself of the health risks of smoking

Avoiding as a Wellness Tool

Things that you want to avoid can also be Wellness Tools. Are there places, people, foods, substances, activities, or thoughts that you want or feel you need to avoid to stay as well as possible? If so, include them on your list of Wellness Tools.

Controversial Wellness Tools

There are controversial things that <u>some</u> people think of as Wellness Tools for themselves like drinking or using substances, eating certain kinds of foods, cutting or smoking. I have found myself at the center of such controversies from time to time. People will want to list things like have a beer, or smoking a cigarette as a Wellness Tool. This is a private, personal list. It is up to the person developing the plan what they want to put on it. And it is up to them to decide when they want to let go of something like smoking or drinking that others might see as bad or negative. <u>Sometimes incremental steps in letting go of certain things are wellness tools, like, I will have only five cigarettes a day instead of the 15 I usually have or I will drink one beer instead of a six pack or I won't cut as deeply this time.</u>

Uncovering More Wellness Tools

You can ask family members, friends, peers, care providers and supporters for ideas for your list of Wellness Tools. If you do this, keep in mind that what you hear from them are only suggestions. Your list of Wellness Tools should only contain things you want to have on it, and things you know you will do and that will work for you. This is your personal list.

In uncovering Wellness Tools, it might help for you to think or write about a good time you had, a day at the beach, or someone's wedding, or going to a play or just relaxing for the day. Then figure out what you did that day that could be considered a Wellness Tool, things like taking pictures, lying in the sun, playing in the waves, and listening to good music.

You may want to carry a small notebook with you for a few days and jot down every wellness tool that comes up, like taking medications and vitamins, eating a good breakfast, doing a short exercise session before going to work, skipping the morning cigarette, buying a flower for the table, or making a special healthy dessert. Then record them on your list of Wellness Tools.

Over time you can add more and more things to your list of Wellness Tools. I am amazed at how long mine has gotten over the years. I continue to use it every time I update my WRAP®, and when I am planning a special day for myself, I review the list and always come up with some great things to do.

WRAP®

Daily Maintenance, Triggers, Early Warning Signs and When Things Are Breaking Down

Now that you have developed your Wellness Toolbox, you will begin developing the first four sections of WRAP®, starting with the Daily Maintenance Plan.

What is the Daily Maintenance Plan?

The *Daily Maintenance Plan* is Section 1 of *WRAP®*. The Daily Maintenance Plan is the section of WRAP® that most people use most often. I have found it to be essential to keeping myself on the right track. It helps me to figure out those things I need to do every day to stay as healthy as possible, and then to plan my days accordingly. It can be surprising to discover how much better you will likely feel taking these positive steps on your own behalf. The Daily Maintenance Plan includes three parts:

- what I am like when I am well
- a list of things I need to do every day to stay well
- a list of things I might need to do to stay well

Your Daily Maintenance Plan will likely change over time as you recover and as you learn new strategies for staying well.

Begin by making a list of words that describe you when you are feeling really well or really good. If you have been feeling badly for a long time, this may be difficult for you. It was difficult for me at first. I couldn't remember feeling well.

It can help if you think back to a time when you really enjoyed yourself. Perhaps it was someone's birthday party or when you went to camp when you were a child. Perhaps it was when you learned something new or spent time with someone you really like. Perhaps you were playing music, listening to music or watching a good movie. Maybe it was a holiday. Looking back at old photos of good times can help you remember what you feel like when you feel well. Then make a list of words that describe how you felt.

Some ideas might be: comfortable, funny, responsible, quiet, sincere, a jokester, capable, smart, retiring, jolly.

What I feel like when I feel well:

_____, _____, _____, _____, _____, _____, _____, _____, _____, _____, _____, _____,

As you are looking through pictures for ideas, you may discover a picture or several pictures of yourself that you like, pictures that show what you are like when you are well. You can include them in this section of your WRAP® for easy reference. You could even have someone take a picture of you now wearing something you like and that feels good on you, in a place you enjoy, doing something you like to do and include that in your WRAP®. Or just a picture of you smiling or looking happy.

You can refer to this section when you need to remind yourself of what you are working toward, and when you can't recall what you feel like when you are feeling well.

Daily Maintenance List

Numerous people never take the time to do the things that make them feel better when they are not feeling well or do things they really enjoy. They often even forget what those things are. They may struggle along, not liking life very much, feeling like they need to reach out for help or have some invasive treatment. Having a Daily Maintenance List can help you avoid this.

Make a list of things you know you must do <u>every day</u> to stay as well as possible and enjoy your life as much as possible. This list should be short enough so that on most days it can be accomplished. It could be just one thing to start off, and then things could be added as time goes on. Or, it could be longer. For instance, one person who had been feeling badly for a long time, had only one thing on his list, walk around the block every day. As he began to feel better, his Daily List got longer. It included things like making himself lunch, taking a shower, making his bed and playing the piano for half an hour.

You can get ideas of things that need to be included on your daily list from your Wellness Toolbox. Or you can carry a small notebook with you for several days and jot down those things that you feel are important for you to do each day. Then you can incorporate them into this list. If you want to, you can ask family members, friends, and care providers for ideas for this list. Do not let others try to make you put things on your list that you do not want on your list. Only you can know what belongs on your list.

If you are just beginning to work on your recovery, keeping up with a daily maintenance list can seem impossible. Keep the daily maintenance list simple and short. An example of things you could have on a short list might be:

- smile at one person
- brush my teeth
- eat a piece of fruit
- take a walk for 10 minutes

A longer list might be as follows:

SAMPLE LIST

- Eat three healthy meals including breakfast
- Drink eight glasses of water
- Get at least half an hour of exercise outside
- Do two relaxation exercises
- Do something creative for at least half and hour, like painting or making music
- Write in my journal for at least 15 minutes
- Talk to another person for 10 minutes

My **Daily Maintenance List**

_____

_____

As you are feeling better and better, you can add new tools to this list.

If you want to, you can develop separate daily maintenance lists for the days when you stay at home and days when you go to work. For instance, a Daily Maintenance List for days when you have to work might include:

- Getting clothes ready to wear the night before
- Getting up at 7:00
- Eating a healthy breakfast
- Checking my appointment book
- Catching up with e-mails, mail and phone messages
- Keeping my desk clear and papers filed
- Taking a 15-minute break mid morning and mid afternoon
- Taking an hour lunch break

You may find it is helpful to make a copy of this list and hang it on your refrigerator door, or in some other convenient place for easy reference throughout the day. Over time you may find you remember all the things you have on this list. If so, you won't have to refer to it as often.

Many people find they have to update this part of the list often as they learn more about themselves, learn more wellness tools, and as they recover and their lives change.

Things I Might Need To Do to Stay Well

The third part of the *Daily Maintenance Plan* is to make a list of things you might need to do, or that it would be good to do on a particular day, things you don't need to do every day but, if you need to do them and don't, it might cause you extra discomfort or stress. This includes things that need to be done from time to time.

Again, refer back to your list of Wellness Tools for ideas. In addition you can look around your home for ideas of things that might need to be done. Include things that you enjoy. This list will probably be longer than your daily maintenance list.

Examples of things you might include on this list:
- Paying bills
- Watering the plants
- Getting the groceries
- Cleaning the house
- Doing the laundry
- Vacuuming
- Making an appointment with my doctor
- Contacting a family member
- Changing the sheets on my bed
- Cleaning the closets
- Putting away my winter clothes
- Getting a massage
- Spending time with a counselor or case manager
- Going to the beach
- Going to a movie
- Attending a special event in my community, like a concert or play
- Signing up for an educational course
- Birdwatching
- Window shopping

Triggers and Triggers Action Plan

If you are using a binder for Your WRAP, write *"Triggers"* on the next tab. Following the tab add several sheets of paper.

Triggers are external upsetting events or circumstances which produce discomfort. These are things you don't expect and which you have little or no control over, things like family friction, work stress, a baby crying, or loud noises. They are different for everyone. Things that upset me, like big bills and people yelling, may not upset you at all. But you may be upset by barking dogs and slamming doors. Awareness can help you to prepare ahead for handling these triggers so they don't upset you as much and so you feel better quickly.

Different kinds of triggers may affect you differently. You may feel anxious, sad, confused or worried. You may begin to experience anxiety, panic, discouragement, despair, or negative self-talk. These reactions are normal, but if not dealt with, may cause you to feel worse and worse. Knowing about your susceptibility to triggering events, and developing plans to deal with them, can help you to cope and avoid feeling worse and worse.

It may be hard for you to think of your triggers. Begin by thinking of times in the past when something has happened that made you feel badly. In trying to uncover your triggers, answering the following questions might help.

What are things that might happen around your home on any given day that might make you feel badly (getting an upsetting phone call, or a phone call from a specific person, seeing troubling things on TV, hearing a noise in the night that you can't identify, having computer difficulties, appliances that don't work and a messy or cluttered space)?

What kinds of things might happen when you are out in your community that might be a trigger (seeing someone who has treated you badly in the past, someone being rude to you, hearing a siren, seeing an accident, missing the bus, not getting a seat on the subway, having to wait in a long line)?

If you have a job, what would be some employment related triggers (tasks to do that are difficult for you, falling behind in some of your work, more to do than you can possibly do, co-workers or employers who are unkind and treat you badly, difficulty getting to work on time, being late)?

You may have some triggers related to health care. Some ideas include:
Getting a shot

Learning that you have an illness or disorder

Care providers or technicians treating you badly

Undergoing an uncomfortable or undignified procedure

Surgery

Think about all your health care providers and the places you go for treatment to get more ideas on things that could happen there that might upset you.

Personal relationships, including relationships with supporters like close friends and family members, can often be a source of stress. Think about the various people that are important to you in your life. How could this connection be a stressor? Some of the following ideas might help you think about this:

One of them treats you badly

You have a disagreement or argument with one of them

One of them is sick or dies

You are having trouble getting in touch with one of them

Someone tells you they don't care about you any more

You fall in love

You are expecting a child

Ending a relationship

Being criticized or blamed

What are the other circumstances of you life that you could think about that might help you to uncover triggers? Some ideas include:

Service in the military

Having a disability

Being in an accident

Having cultural, racial, sexual orientation, political or economic differences from the people around you

Living in an unsafe neighborhood

Being a trauma or abuse victim

You may want to ask others for ideas for this list. Talking with peers, friends, family members, health care providers and others might help you to uncover more of your triggers. However, always keep in mind that you only need to discuss your WRAP, what you put in it, and whether you even have a WRAP, with the people of your choice.

You may not think of all your triggers right now. You can always add triggers to your list as you become aware of them.

You may even want to remove some things from your list if you discover they are no longer upsetting to you. Keep in mind that triggers are personal. Things that may be upsetting to you may not be upsetting to others, and things that upset others may be easy for you to deal with.

You can get more ideas for your list of triggers from the following list of common triggers.

Traumatic news events
Work stress
Family friction
Spending too much time alone
Financial problems
Angry outbursts by others
Broken promises
Roadside debris
Fast drivers
Being asked to work long hours
Being judged
Sexual harassment
Sustained loud noises
Aggressive sounding noises
Being condemned/shunned by others
Being around certain people
Reminders of abandonment or deprivation
Someone being bossy
Things related to substance abuse
A stormy day

My list of **Triggers**

_____

_____

_____

_____

When identifying triggers, list those that are likely to occur from time to time. Avoid projecting all the many catastrophic things that might happen to anyone but that are impossible to predict, such as war, a natural disaster, or a huge personal loss. If those things were to occur, you would use the actions you describe in the Triggers Action Plan you are about to develop more often, and increase the length of time you use them.

Triggers Action Plan

You have now written down events or circumstances that, if they happen, may produce reactions that are, or may be, uncomfortable and upsetting to you.

On the next page of your binder, write *"Triggers Action Plan."* Under that write: "If any of these events or circumstances come up, I use the following Wellness Tools to keep me feeling well or to help me feel better." Then list ideas from your Wellness Toolbox that you can do when these triggers come up, that will help you to work your way through this difficult time, and avoid further repercussions, like deep sadness, severe anxiety, unusual behaviors, being unable to sleep and having nightmares.

How you respond to your triggers may differ depending on your circumstances. It is important to have lots of options on this list to address the many different situations you might experience.

For example, if you were riding on a bus and see a bad accident it may be very upsetting to you. It would probably be impossible for you to talk to a friend about it, to play your guitar, work in your garden or get some exercise at that time. Instead you could take a few deep breaths, visualize a beautiful place or a special time in your life, meditate or pray, or talk to a person sitting near you.

If you are at home and your computer breaks down, you could troubleshoot possible problems, call the repair line, take a break to do some reading, take a fast walk around the block, or ask for help from a friend.

Perhaps your doctor told you that you had diabetes. This was very upsetting. You asked your doctor questions about what that meant. When you got home you called a friend to talk about it. Then you looked it up on the internet to get more information. Then you spent the rest of the day doing something you enjoy and put off doing more about it until the next day.

Maybe you saw an old friend when you were in town. The friend didn't seem to know who you were and ignored you. You felt badly. You stopped at a lunch stand and had a cup of tea. You took time out to walk in a nearby park. You kept repeating positive affirmations about yourself over and over in your mind. When you got home you called an understanding friend and told him about it. You spent the evening listening to music you enjoy.

Or perhaps you saw an article in the newspaper about an event that was similar to something that happened to you in the past. It brought up lots of bad memories. It was hard to stop thinking about it. You wrote in your journal for 15 minutes and took time out to read a good book.

You took a walk with a friend. You arranged to spend the evening babysitting for a friend's children, something you always enjoy.

If you know in advance that the anniversary of your parent's death is coming up, you could plan the day to include lots of Wellness Tools that will make the day easier for you.

If you want to, ask friends and family members for their ideas. You could ask for ideas in a support group like a vet to vet group, a weight loss support group or a grief support group. After getting input from others, include in your list what you feel is best for you. Remember to only use what you feel is best for you.

You can get more ideas by attending workshops and lectures, reading self-help books, talking to your health care provider, and by talking to other people who have had experiences similar to yours.

Spend some time writing your triggers action plan. You may want to take a break from it and come back to it later. You can always add new ideas as you learn about and try them. If you find that some things are not helpful, you can take them off your list.

Triggers Action Plan

_____

_____

_____

_____

_____

_____

_____

_____

_____

_____

You can begin to use this section of your WRAP right away. Most people review their WRAP every day when they have first developed it. As you do that, you will become more and more aware of the triggers as they happen in your daily life. You will also become more familiar with the actions you can take to keep yourself from feeling badly and help yourself feel better. Over time you will not need to review your plan as much because you will remember all the options that you have and take action as you need to.

"Big Triggers"

When I talk with groups about identifying triggers, I encourage people to focus on those things that might happen on any given day, like someone being rude to you, having computer problems, having a disagreement with a friend or missing the bus. I caution people not to "catastrophize," not to think of all the horrific things that might happen like a big accident, a serious illness or injury, a big storm with lots of destruction, losing your home or losing someone very close to you. I suggested that if one of those horrible things did happen, you could refer to your list of wellness tools and use them intensively.

But I was not really speaking from experience. Unfortunately now I can speak from experience. I want to share with you what I have learned about WRAP® and the intensive use of Wellness Tools in the last three years since I learned that three of my treasured grandchildren have a kidney disease. This disease meant that over time their kidneys would stop functioning, and they would need kidney transplants and that there would be lots of other health challenges along the way.

I first learned of this on a March afternoon three years ago. I knew my 13 year old grandson was not feeling well and had been to the doctor for blood tests. I figured they would sort out the problem and all would be well. So when the phone rang as I was using my chi machine (one of my wellness tools), I let it ring and continued with what I was doing. Like me, you have all probably been reminded that you should not be a slave to your phone. I was practicing it that day. But as soon as I finished, I checked to see if there was a message. There was. It was my daughter-in-law. She was clearly frantic. She said that something was really wrong with my grandson and they were on their way to the ER. I immediately called and she said, "They don't know anything except that this is really, really serious."

I was home alone. No one to talk to and feeling really scared. My husband was making maple syrup with my son and out of cell phone reach. From my Wellness Tools list, "I realized, I need to be with someone." So I got in my car and went and found my husband and son and stayed with them until my husband and I could go home and get more news. When we got home, we learned that my grandson's kidneys had stopped functioning, that they were giving him fluids and would decide the next day how to proceed.

The next morning we got in the car and went to be with my son, his wife and my grandson — another Wellness Tool. We spent long hours talking to doctors about what was going on, learning everything we could.

Over time we learned that Samuel would need a transplant and so would two of his sisters. Through this time, fraught with worry, I did the best I could to stick with my Daily Maintenance Plan, eating right, getting exercise, doing relaxation techniques, doing something fun each day that I possible could. And whenever I could, I added in the things that sustain me – extra time with family and friends, a long and vigorous hike, a good book to read, and lots of what I have come to call diversionary activities.

The first of many extremely challenging days came when my grandson had his transplant and my son was the donor. It was of course scary leading up to it. I knew I would be sitting for long hours waiting for word. So I set myself up with a knitting project that would keep me well occupied in the hospital waiting room. But things did not go well. Both my son and grandson had major complications. As the hours went by with little word and reassurance, I found myself getting more and more anxious. Each of us who was waiting tried to deal with this in our own way. I paced up and down the hospital corridors. Mile after mile. A nurse accompanied me for a time. It was all I could do. And it worked. It relieved enough anxiety to keep me going. And finally, after seeing my son and my grandson, and talking at length to family members and health care providers, I was able to relax a bit and breathe.

Since that day there have been many similar days when the children have been very sick and we were not sure what was going to happen. There have been two more transplants. That first transplant has failed and another is needed. Through all of this, everyone in the family has gotten more adept at using wellness tools, although not everybody calls them that. I have found that I need some kind of body work at least every other week, but every week is best. I need to keep up regular appointments with my counselor. I need to have regular face to face contact with the children. I have several people I am very close to that know me well and comfort me whenever I need it. I have an e-mail circle of friends, family members and acquaintances that I reach out to. Those return e-mail messages have been terrific. I have sent out to my Facebook friends and feel so comforted by expressions of concern, thoughts and prayers from these special friends.

I keep working on this all the time, learning more and more. My WRAP has become more and more important to me in my life. I have found that the easiest way for me to keep it in the forefront and to keep it updated, is by using the Build Your Own WRAP e-learning program. Then each time I make a change I can send myself a copy.

So it can be done. But it is not easy. It is the hardest thing I have done in my life.

Early Warning Signs Action Plan

The third section of WRAP is Early Warning Signs and Early Warning Signs Action Plan. On the tab for this section of your binder (or notebook or computer file if one of these is your method for creating a WRAP) write *"Early Warning Signs"*. Following the tab, add several sheets of paper.

Early Warning Signs are those internal signs that you notice when you are starting to feel badly. These signs may be unrelated to reactions to stressful situations, or they may indeed result from a difficult situation. Sometimes, you just aren't sure why you are experiencing these early warning signs. You just know that they are there.

Despite your best attention to your Daily Maintenance Plan and to reducing your reactions to Triggers, you may still begin to experience Early Warning Signs. These changes indicate the need for further action.

On the first sheet after the heading *"Early Warning Signs"*, make a list of those internal clues, which indicate you are starting to feel badly. You might not notice these signs at first, because they can be subtle. However, when you recognize them, they signify you likely need to take some further action to prevent things from getting worse or breaking down.

Examples of Early Warning Signs that others have reported, that might help you to think of your own early warning signs, include:

anxiety
lack of motivation
the beginning irrational thought patterns
increased negativity
aches and pains
overeating
smoking too much
being too quiet
feelings of abandonment or rejection
not wanting to answer the phone or the door
avoiding people you know on the street
forgetfulness
feeling slowed down or speeded up
avoiding others or isolating
feeling unconnected to your body
weepiness without a cause you can think of

It may not be easy to name all of your Early Warning Signs. Like others, you may ignore or overlook them. It may help to think of times in the past when you have had mental health difficulties, and recall how you felt at that time. It might also help to ask your counselor, other care providers, family members, friends and peers for ideas. Keep in mind that ideas from others are only suggestions. You are the only person who can know how you feel and what you experience.

You can add early warning signs to this list anytime you become aware of them.

Reviewing your Early Warning Signs regularly can help you to be more aware of them, allowing you to take action before they worsen.

The next step in developing your WRAP is your Early Warning Signs Action Plan.
On the next page of your binder, write *"Early Warning Signs Action Plan"*. Under that write: "If I notice any of my early warning signs, I will do some of the activities listed on the next page to help me deal with them so that I feel better quickly and avoid feeling worse." On this page, you will list ideas of how you can respond when Early Warning Signs come up, so you can take appropriate action.

How you respond to your Early Warning Signs may differ depending on your situation. Have lots of options on this list to address the many different feelings and reactions you might experience.

You will develop your Early Warning Signs Action Plan by reviewing your Wellness Toolbox. Consider each item in your toolbox thoughtfully, to decide if it might help if you were experiencing Early Warning Signs. If you think it would help, list it in your Early Warning Signs Action Plan. For instance, you may decide that Wellness Tools like relaxation, exercise, support groups, a warm bath, gardening, or getting a medication check would be helpful to you if you are experiencing early warning signs. Perhaps extra rest, planning a special diet, or seeing your counselor would be your choices.

Following is a sample plan for Early Warning Signs. It will give you some ideas for creating your own plan.

<u>Sample Plan</u>
If I notice any of my Early Warning Signs, I will do some or all of the following activities to help myself feel better and to avoid feeling worse.
- Talk to a peer, healthcare provider, family member or friend
- Do the things on my Daily Maintenance List, whether I feel like it or not
- Do at least three 10-minute relaxation exercises each day

- Write in my journal for at least 15 minutes each day
- Spend at least one hour involved in an activity I enjoy
- Ask others to take over my household responsibilities for the day
- Go to a support group meeting, if there is one
- Write in my journal for at least 15 minutes each day

You could choose to list things like:
- Go fishing or camping
- Read a good book or magazine
- Listen to music or go to a play
- Talk a walk or ride a bike
- Spend time with my pet
- Dance or draw
- Exercise or take a day off from exercising

As you are developing an Early Warning Signs Action Plan, you could choose to ask friends and family members for their ideas. You could ask for ideas in a support group you attend like a vet to vet group, a weight loss support group or a grief support group. After getting input from group members, include in your plan only those that you feel will work for you.

It may help to have a conversation with your health care providers to get more ideas. You may want to attend some workshops and lectures, read some self-help books, and talk with other people who have had experiences similar to yours.

Add new ideas as you learn about and try them. If you find that some things are not helpful, take them off your list. If you use this plan and it doesn't help you to feel better, revise your plan using your Wellness Toolbox and other ideas as you learn about and try them.

Many people read their WRAP often. Some people do so daily, especially when first starting out. Just like the earlier sections of WRAP, as you review this section on Early Warning Signs, you will become more and more aware of what clues to watch for in your daily life. You will become familiar with the actions you must take to keep yourself from feeling worse and to help yourself get better. This review will help you remember to follow the instructions you have written to help things become better rather than worse.

When Things Are Breaking Down and Action Plan

The forth section of WRAP is When Things Are Breaking Down and Action Plan.

On the tab for this section of your binder (or notebook or computer file if you are using one of those) write "When Things Are Breaking Down". Following the tab, add several sheets of paper.

On the first sheet after that heading, you will make a list of those signs that, for you, mean things have worsened and you might be close to a crisis (that time when you need others to take care of you). Your list might be similar to the one for Early Warning Signs. However, what makes this section different is the intensity, duration, and addition of other signs appearing at the same time. Everyone wants to avoid a crisis. This section is as close as you can get to being in a crisis without actually being in a crisis. Others have found that, by identifying the signs that things are much worse, "breaking down," and taking action in their own behalf, they can avert a potential crisis. Using their Wellness Tools, they can work their way back to wellness.

The first step is identifying signs that Things Are Breaking Down. These are thoughts, feelings, and behaviors that are very distracting and uncomfortable to you. What may mean things are breaking down to one person may be only an early warning sign to another , or a crisis indicator for someone else. In the past, you may have considered the signs you will identify in this section to be signs of a crisis. But many people have found that, by taking assertive action in their own behalf, they can reduce and relieve these signs before they need others to take over responsibility for their care.

Some examples of When Things Are Breaking Down include:
    feeling very needy, or not feeling anything at all
    being unable to sleep, or sleeping all the time
    driving too fast
    substance abuse
    thoughts of self-harm
    seeing things that are not there
    feeling oversensitive or fragile
    increased pain
    obsessed with negative thoughts
    paranoia
    taking out your anger on others
    staying home from working
    not caring about anything
    not interested in things I usually enjoy
    unreasonable anger and hostility
    yelling at others
    disrespectful

racing thoughts

thoughts of self-harm

avoiding eating

inability to slow down

unable to sleep (for how long?)

dissociation: blacking out, spacing out, losing time

chain smoking

As with other sections of the plan, you can get ideas for this section from care providers, family members, friends and peers. Thinking of difficult times in the past may help as well. In addition, add to your list as you become aware of other signs that things are breaking down.

When Things are Breaking Down Action Plan

On the next page of your binder, write "*When Things Are Breaking Down Action Plan.*" Under that, write: "If any of these signs come up, I will do <u>all</u> of the activities listed on the next page to avoid a crisis."

On this page, create a plan that is <u>directive</u>. It should have <u>few choices</u> and <u>clear directions</u>. The goal is to reduce and relieve your signs when they have progressed to this point. To achieve this goal, it is important to have clear and focused instructions about what steps to take to prevent things from getting worse, at this time when you can still take some action to help yourself.

As with previous sections, go back to your Wellness Toolbox. Review each tool carefully, considering if it would be helpful in this section of your plan. Following is a sample plan for When Things Are Breaking Down. It may give you some ideas for creating your own plan.

<u>Sample Plan</u> (this is just a sample, your plan will be specific to your need)
If I notice any signs that things are breaking down, <u>I will do all of the following</u> until I feel better and am no longer have signs that Things are Breaking Down:
- Call my doctor or other health care provider, ask for and follow their instructions
- Call my supporters and talk as long as I need to or as long as they can
- Arrange for someone to stay with me around the clock until I feel better
- Give my medications, check book, credit cards, and car keys to my sister for safe keeping
- Do everything on my Daily Maintenance Plan
- Arrange and take at least three days off from any responsibilities including work
- Have at least two exchange listening sessions with a supporter daily
- Do three deep breathing relaxation exercises a day

- Do two focusing exercises
- Write in my journal for at least one half hour

Your Action Plan for When Things Are Breaking Down might include additional choices like:
- Creative Activities, like drawing, singing, or writing poetry
- Exercises, like jogging, sit-ups, taking a walk, or swimming

It may be helpful to you in thinking of things to include in your When Things are Breaking Down Action Plan to remember times in the past when you have had a really hard time and things began breaking down. Think of what you did at that time to help yourself . List those ideas in your When Things Are Breaking Down Action Plan.

Again, you can choose to ask friends and family for their ideas.

You may find that this part of the plan is harder for you to write than other parts. It may bring up difficult feelings. You may want to take a break from it and come back to it later.

Add new ideas as you learn about and try them. If you find that some things are not helpful when you use them, you can take them off your list.

Just like the earlier sections of WRAP, as you review this section on When Things Are Breaking Down, you will become more and more aware of what signs to watch for in your daily life. You will become familiar with the actions you need to take to keep yourself from feeling worse and to help yourself get better. This review will help you remember to follow the instructions you have written if you experience a time when things get really tough.

In Conclusion

You have now completed The Wellness Toolbox and the first four sections of Wellness Recovery Action Planning. The next chapters will lead you through the process of developing a Crisis Plan, or Advance Directive and a Post Crisis Plan. Then, the final chapter in this section will give you ideas on how to use your Wellness Recovery Action Plan as a guide to daily living.

WRAP®

Advance Directive, or Crisis Planning

This chapter will walk you, step by step, through the process of developing an Advance Directive, also known as a Crisis Plan.

In this chapter, I will focus on Advance Directives/Crisis Plans for mental health issues. However, your Crisis Plan/Advance Directive can address only mental health issues, or it can address medical issues as well. The same form can be used and each section of the plan can include responses that address both issues.

What is a Crisis Plan or Advance Directive?

A Crisis Plan or Advance Directive is a plan you develop by yourself, or with the assistance of others. It instructs others on how to provide you with care and support when you are having such a difficult time (crisis) that you cannot take care of yourself or make good decisions on your own behalf.

The sections of the WRAP Crisis Plan or Advance Directive are:
Section 1. What I am like when I am feeling well
Section 2. Indicators that I need assistance from others
Section 3 Who takes over and who doesn't
Section 4 Medications that help and those that don't
Section 5 Treatments that help and those that don't
Section 6 A home/community/respite care plan
Section 7 Acceptable and unacceptable treatment facilities
Section 8 Thing that others can do that would help and things that won't help
Section 9 Chores that need to be taken care of
Section 10 When the Crisis Plan is no longer needed

Having your own Crisis Plan keeps you in control even when it feels like things are out of control. Supporters appreciate Crisis Plans because, rather than trying to figure out what to do, it gives them the information they need to help you stay safe, feel better and recover quickly.

Why would you want to develop a Crisis Plan?

Most of us like to keep our lives under our own control. However, unanticipated circumstances such as the onset of severe mental health difficulties, a life tragedy, an illness or an accident can and do occur in everyone's lives. An Advance Directive will tell others what to do and when to do it, keeping the person who developed the plan in control, even when it seems like things are out of control.

Without an Advance Directive, well-meaning people may step in if they feel you are having a difficult time, and do things that you do not want to have done. They may treat you in ways that are not helpful to you and may even be harmful.

When is a good time to develop an Advance Directive or Crisis Plan?

Develop your Advance Directive after you have developed a Wellness Toolbox and the first four sections of WRAP: Daily Maintenance Plan, Triggers, Early Warning Signs and When Things are Breaking Down. This work facilitates the process of developing an Advance Directive by helping you gain experience, self knowledge and confidence that will guide the Advance Directive process. The Wellness Toolbox will give you ideas that you can use as you develop your Advance Directive.

Using the first four sections of WRAP as your guide to daily living helps assure that you will not get into a situation where others need to take over responsibility for your care. However, in spite of your best planning and action, you may find yourself in a difficult situation where others will need to take over responsibility for your care. You may feel as though you are totally out of control. Your Advance Directive will tell others, the people of your choice, how to help you, keeping you in control. Because you have developed this Advance Directive, they will know what to do, saving everyone time and frustration, while ensuring that your needs will be met and that you will get better as quickly as possible.

Who Develops your Advance Directive?

It is essential that you, the person whose Advance Directive this is, develop the plan. While in the past, other people may have done this for you, it has been found that plans developed by other people for you are not effective. You know more about yourself than anyone else, and only you can make decisions about things like who you want to take over, and what you want them to do. You can ask others for assistance and support in this process, but what's in the plan must be up to you.

How do you ensure that your Advance Directive will work?

When you are developing this plan, make sure you develop a plan that can work. Avoid including directives to others that may be really impractical, not possible, that may get in the way of you quickly getting the attention and treatment you need, or may compromise your life.

The Advance Directive is different from other parts of your WRAP because you will be giving it to others and they will have to be able to understand it. Make sure it is clear, easy to understand, and legible. Clearly specify times and amounts where appropriate. Describe situations and possible events as clearly as possible. Err on the side of too many words and redundancy, rather than on not having enough information.

What kind of forms do you use to develop a Crisis Plan?

There are many different forms that you can use to develop a Crisis Plan. Most of these forms have been developed by mental health agencies and organizations. The form that is used in WRAP® was developed by a group of people who experience mental health difficulties. There is a copy of this plan at the end of this chapter. I suggest you make several copies of it so you have a working copy and then a clean copy for your final plan. Always keep a copy on hand so you can easily update your plan. You can download a hard copy of this form at http://mentalhealthrecovery. com/recovery_crisisplanning.php to use as your guide as you work on this course.

There are several options for developing your plan. You can use paper forms or you can develop it using forms on a computer. I have found that the best way for me to store my Advance Directive (and the rest of my WRAP), easily update it and easily send new copies out to my supporters, is using the Build Your Own WRAP Program at https://wrap.essentiallearning.com/Register.aspx. There is a small charge. However, some mental health agencies offer free access to this program. You can see if that is an option for you.

The advantages of the written method are that it is easiest for people who are uncomfortable with computers or don't have access to a computer. However, it is difficult to change a written plan. Each time you make a change in your plan you have to rewrite at least the pages you change and perhaps the whole plan. Then you have to make new copies and give them to all your supporters. Even though you have the copies clearly dated, people may confuse old copies with new ones, even if you ask them to discard old copies.

Is your Advance Directive a legal document?

In some places the Advance Directive is a legal document that must be followed by health care providers if at all possible. In any case, it is an essential guide to anyone who is trying to support you if you are having serious mental health difficulties.

Contact your state office of protection and advocacy to learn the legal status of Mental Health Advance Directives in your state. They will be listed in your phone book, you can get their phone number from your state's governor's hotline, or you can look it up on line. You can also request copies of any Advance Directive templates by mail or e-mail. You can revise the advance directive form in this chapter to meet your state's requirements.

Even in places where the Advance Directive is not considered a legal document, you can help to assure that it will be honored by signing it in the presence of two witnesses, having it notarized, and having it signed by an attorney.

Developing an Advance Directive can take a lot of time and thought. You may choose to work on your Advance Directive on your own, with the help of a supporter or care provider, or in a WRAP® group. The group can be most helpful because you get ideas from others in the group. It can take many hours over several months to develop this plan.

Once you have completed your Advance Directive, give copies of it to the people you name on this plan as your supporters.

Important things to keep in mind as you develop your Advance Directive

1. This is your plan and no one else should tell you what you should or should not put in it.
2. It needs to be written so others can easily understand it.
3. Writing an advance directive can be difficult. It may remind you of times you would rather forget. If you start feeling badly as you develop your plan, set it aside for a time and do something interesting or fun that will divert your attention.
4. Write your plan slowly over time when you are feeling quite well. Ask others for ideas, assistance and support.

Working on the Crisis Plan or Advance Directive

Now you will begin working on the actual plan. Again, the parts of the plan are:

Section 1. What I am Like when I am Feeling Well

Section 2. Indicators that I Need Assistance from Others

Section 1. What I am Like when I am feeling well

If you have developed the first four parts of your WRAP®, you developed a list of words at the beginning of your Daily Maintenance Plan that describes what you are like when you are well. You can copy this section into the beginning of your Crisis Plan. If you don't have a WRAP®, you will need to develop this section. Make a list of words that describe what you are like when you are well.

You can include a picture of yourself when you are feeling well. You could also attach a picture of yourself when you are doing something you enjoy. For instance, if in your picture others see that you are generally well groomed and people see that you have not taken care of your personal hygiene and are sloppily dressed, they will know this is out of character for you.

This section will help others understand you better, and be clear about what is a sign that you are having a difficult time, and what is not   —   perhaps that you are just having a hard time but can deal with it yourself. For someone who doesn't know you well, or at all, like someone at an agency or treatment center, this is very important.

In addition, having this reminder of what you are like when you are well keeps you focused on wellness and what you can do to achieve that, rather than on illness and things that are "wrong."

Some descriptive words that can used for this section include:
   happy
   outgoing
   calm
   thoughtful
   gregarious
   talkative
   quiet

introverted

shy

A paragraph that describes yourself might be as follows:

When I am well, I am calm and rather quiet. I like to be with people but often I don't say much. I would rather listen to what others have to say and interject a comment here and there. I like to read a lot and may spend several hours a day reading. My dog is a big part of my life and I love taking her for long walks and playing with her in the park. I have a few good friends that I like a lot and when I am with them I tend to be more outgoing. I tend to be a "night owl" and have a hard time getting going in the morning. Others say that I am capable and responsible, the kind of person you can count on. I dress casually but always look neat and keep my apartment tidy and uncluttered.

If this is hard for you, you can get ideas for words to put on your list from other people in the group, family members, peers and friends.

Section 2. Indicators that I need assistance from others

In this section, describe the signs that would indicate to others that they need to assist you, make decisions for you and take over responsibility for your care. In developing this section, be thoughtful and ask yourself, "When do I really need others to step in and take over for me?" It may help to think back to hard times in the past. It may not be pleasant to do, but it can give you critical information that will help you make this section useful to you and to the people who care about you.

In the past the decision to step in and take over has probably been made by others without input from you. People may have stepped in and taken over while you were in the midst of doing all the things you knew you needed to do to help yourself feel better. In fact, you may have already been feeling much better. You may have known that you were in the "When things are breaking down" section of your WRAP® and did not need anyone to take over at this time. Having this plan and having it clearly written, can help prevent that from happening.

Each of your supporters needs to understand this part of your plan and be willing to step in only when you have these signs.

These signs must be described well, so it is clear to others that you need help, even though you may not tell them you need help, or you may even tell them you don't need help, or to stay away from you.

Some signs others have suggested include:

- being unable to recognize or correctly identify family members and friends
- uncontrollable pacing, unable to stay still for 4 hours
- not combing my hair (for how many days?)
- not cooking or doing any housework (for how many days?)
- thinking I am someone I am not, someone famous
- thinking I have the ability to do something I can't do (like fly)
- abusive, destructive or violent behavior, toward self, others, or property
- shoplifting
- making sexual advances toward people I don't know
- spending large amounts of money (how much?) on things I don't need
- giving away money and possessions to people I don't know
- not getting out of bed (for how long?)
- refusing to eat or drink (for how long?)

When people are working on this part of the plan, they often recall difficult times they have had in the past. This can be upsetting. If you notice you are starting to feel upset as you work on this part of the plan, put it away for a while and work on some other part of the plan, or take a break and do something you really enjoy, like reading a good book or calling a friend.

It may be easier for you if, when you are working on this section, you ask a supporter to be with you to discuss ideas and even exchange listen with you.

Don't rush this process. Take your time. You will get more ideas for this list as you think about it over time.

Section 3. Who takes over and who doesn't

The success of this plan is dependent on the supporters who implement it. You will want to give careful consideration to who you want these people to be. You will want them to be people who care about you and like you, who you trust to follow your instructions in this plan, who make good decisions, who you enjoy being with, and with whom you feel comfortable sharing the hardest times in your life.

These are the people you want to take over for you when the signs you listed in the previous section, **Indicators That I need Assistance from Others** come up. They will do the things you need and want them to do that are described in other sections of the plan.

You, the person developing the plan, and only you, can decide who these people should be. Others might think certain people should be on your list, but only you can know who you trust implicitly to play this important role in your life. Don't give in if others try to make you list certain people on your plan that you don't think would be helpful, and might not be willing to follow your plan.

To help you with the task of deciding who you want to be your supporters, you may want to make a list of the attributes you would like in your supporters, things like:

> patience
> understanding
> generally available
> fun
> competent
> reliable
> trustworthy
> calm
> compassionate
> easy to get along with
> makes good decisions
> responsible

You may want to discuss this with others to get clarity for yourself around this issue.

Before listing someone as a supporter in this part of your plan, talk with them about what you'd like from them. Make sure they understand and agree to be in the plan. They can be family members, friends, peers or health care providers. When you first develop this plan your list may be mostly health care providers. But as you work on developing your support system, try to change the list so you rely more heavily on family members and friends, as they are most available. Your health care providers may change over time, have limited availability and may have boundary restrictions that would keep them from doing some things on your plan, like coming to your home and staying with you. These supporters need to be committed to following the plans you have written.

Have at least five people, and more if possible, on your list of supporters. If you have only one or two, they might not be available when you really need them, like when they go on vacation or are sick, and then you wouldn't have anyone. If you have five, it is likely that at least several would be available. Let people know that you are willing to be their supporter if they would like you to fill that role.

If, right now, you only have one or two supporters, list them in your plan. Then, using the information in the support chapter of this book, work on developing new connections and supporters whom you can add to this list over time. It will strengthen your plan and enrich your life.

Also include here a list of people you <u>do not</u> want to be involved in any way if you are having a crisis. They may be people you like a lot, but that don't do well in hard times. They may become agitated, controlling, judgmental, threatening or scared. They may try to make you do things that are not in your plan or that you know won't help. They may be people who have treated you badly in the past.

You will need to be very clear about this. You may want to include the reason why you do not want a specific person involved. Talk with your supporters about the importance of respecting your wishes in this regard. You may get pressure from a family member or friend who wants to be involved, but who you do not want to have involved, so you have to be firm.

You may be concerned that you will hurt someone's feelings if you do not include them on your list. Try not to focus on that. In a crisis, you need to be dealing only with people you can trust to treat you well and do for you what you need. If people are offended by not being included, try to remember that this plan is about you and your safety and wellness, and that you need to do what is right for you.

You may also want to include in this part of the plan a description of how you want any disputes resolved, disputes that may come up between your supporters as they try to do their best to assist and support you as you want them to.

Some ideas for this are:
> Take a vote and the majority rules
> Come up with an option that everyone can agree on
> A particular person, like your spouse, makes all final decisions

Section 4. Medications that help and those that don't

The information in this section is straightforward. It includes key information your supporters may need about care providers and medications. This includes:
- the names, roles, and phone numbers of all care providers like doctors, counselors, case managers, vocational counselors, etc., and under what circumstances they should be contacted
- the names of your insurance providers and key numbers

- the name and phone number of your pharmacy (To avoid medication interactions, use only one pharmacy for all your medications. Make sure they have a complete listing of all the medications you are using on their computer, and that they check for possible negative interactions each time you get a new prescription or change doses.)
- medications you are taking, why you are taking them, dosage, time administered and how you take them
- medications that are acceptable to you if needed, why they might be needed and how it can be arranged to get them (who should be contacted)
- medications that must be avoided and why (allergies, side effects, personal preference)
- any other health care preparations you are using like supplements or creams, why you are using them, how much you use and when you use it

Include here any other instructions that you feel would be helpful to your supporters to ensure that medication and supplement issues are taken care of properly.

Section 5. Treatments that help and those that don't

In this section, list those treatments that have been helpful in the past and that could be used now, and how and when they could be used. Include the name of the person (or people) who provides or arranges for this treatment. This could include things like acupuncture and various kinds of massage.

Also list those treatments you would not want. The one that comes up here most often is electroconvulsive therapy (ECT). Some people have found it to be very helpful, while others do not want it under any circumstance. If you are not sure how you feel about a specific treatment, find out more about it before including it in your plan. Ask your health care providers and mental health organizations for information, look it up on the internet or at your library, and ask other people who have had this treatment. Then make up your own mind about it.

To be absolutely sure you do not receive a treatment you do not want, make a strong statement about it in your plan. It could be, "I do not want electroconvulsive therapy under any circumstances. If anyone is insisting that I have this treatment, please do whatever you need to do to prevent it from happening."

Section 6. Home/Community/Respite Plan

Some people see this section of the plan and say, "I don't need to bother with that" and skip over it. Don't do that. This is one of the most powerful pieces of this plan. It deserves your time and attention so you can develop a clear plan for staying at home or in the community rather than in a hospital when you are in a crisis.

Why is this important?
- Most people are much more comfortable at home and can recover more quickly in a familiar place.
- There may be places in the community where you can stay for a time, supporterd by your peers and/or caring staff members.
- Being in a strange place with people you don't know, people who may be having a difficult time as well, and with staff who don't know and understand you, can make your recovery more difficult.
- In today's world of limited health care options, hospitalization may not be possible for you.
- There may not be any appropriate hospital facilities in your area.
- You will be cared for by people you already know rather than by strangers.
- Your family members, friends and peers have a deeper understanding of you and your situation.

To find out what options are available for you, you will need to talk to others and do some research. Ask a supporter or care provider for assistance and support if you feel you need it. Take the following steps

1. Talk to the people on your support list about how much time they can spend with you and what they can do for you if you are having a crisis.

2. Talk to mental health agencies and organizations, and your care providers, to find out what options are available to you in your community. You may find that there is:
A peer-run respite center where you can go and be supported by your peers until you are feeling better. Visit the center and talk with the staff to see if this might be an option for you. Most of these require that you have an interview with them, in advance, in order to take advantage of this option. You may want to do that at this time.

A low-key facility that does not include medical care where you can go and be supported and cared for until you are feeling better.

A program where you can stay in a motel or hotel with a mental health worker until you are feeling better.

A day program in the community where you could go in the daytime, with friends and family staying with you and supporting you in the evening and through the night.

Use the information you have learned to develop your plan. You may want to include several different alternatives that are acceptable to you in case one or the other doesn't work out (For example, there is no space in the respite center).

Examples of possible plans

1. If I am in a crisis as defined in Section 2 of this plan, I want my supporters (as they have agreed), to come and stay with me in my home, setting up a schedule among themselves that works for them. I will not be left alone. No supporter will leave until the next one arrives, even if I tell them it is OK to leave. They will do the things for me that I have written in other parts of this plan. If they feel that I am not safe and that they cannot assure my safety they need to call the local crisis team and arrange for me to be transported to a safe facility.

2. If I am in a crisis as defined in Section 2 of this plan, I would like one of my supporters to call the crisis respite center where I am registered and arrange for me to be taken there until I feel well enough to come home. When I get home, I would like my supporters to arrange that a supporter is with me at all times until I meet the criteria set out in Section 9 of this plan.

3. If I am in a crisis as defined in Section 2 of this plan, I would like my supporters, working with my psychiatrist to arrange for me to attend the Whole Health Day Treatment Facility during the day and arrange for my supporters to take turns staying with me through the evening and night until I meet the criteria in Section 9 of this plan.

Answering the following questions for yourself might help assure you that you develop a good workable plan:

- Why it is important to have a plan so that you can stay at home or in the community?
- Is hospitalization always an option when you are having a hard time?
- Is hospitalization the best option when you are having a hard time?
- What are the pros and cons of hospitalization?
- What are the advantages of staying home rather than going to the hospital when you are having a difficult time?
- Why might you feel better more quickly if you stayed at home or in the community?
- What would you need in order to stay home when you are having a difficult time?

- What can you do for yourself if you stayed home when you were having a difficult time? What are the Wellness Tools you can use?
- What can others do for you if you stayed home when you were having a difficult time?
- Do you have friends or family members who can take turns providing you with care and support? Who are they?
- Are there any programs in your community that you can attend during the day and be at home in the evening? What are they?
- Are there any respite programs in your community? What are they?
- What health care providers would be available to support you if you stayed at home or in the community during a crisis? How can they help?

If you don't have such a plan in place, you may be taken to a place where you do not want to be, and have treatments that are not helpful or even harmful.

Section 7. Acceptable and unacceptable treatment facilities

In this section of your crisis plan, list the treatment facilities you would like to use if your home/community/respite plan cannot be implemented, family members and friends cannot provide you with care, or if your condition requires hospital care. Your options may be limited by the facilities that are available in your area and your insurance coverage. Also include a list of treatment facilities you would like to avoid – such as places where you received poor care in the past, where you were treated badly or where your Advance Directive/Crisis Plan was not honored. Also include the names of people you would like to take you home when you are released.

In thinking about the facilities you would prefer if you needed to be hospitalized, it may help you to write some words or several paragraphs that would describe the optimal hospital facility for you. For instance, the ideal hospital facility for you might:

Be within 30 miles of your home

Have a wide variety of options for creative activities

Have fewer than 30 patients

Be a place where your doctor has hospital privileges

Provide alternative care like massage and acupuncture

Be clean and attractive

Have single rooms

Be in a rural setting or an urban setting

Offer individual counseling

Have medical treatment available

Have a psychopharmacologist
Have many group opportunities
Be a place that others recommend
Be a place you have been to before and it was satisfactory

You may think of other attributes you want to look for in the best treatment facility or hospital for you.

Section 8. Things that others can do that would help and things that won't

In this section describe for your supporters what they can do that would be helpful. This is a new concept in crisis care. In the past, people did what they thought was best for the person they were caring for. Sometimes it was helpful. Often it was not helpful. Sometimes it was even harmful. The only options considered may have been medications, hospitalization, seclusion and restraint. (Medications may still be on your list of things that will help. Be specific about kinds and amounts.)

Spend some time thinking about this, and perhaps even discussing it with friends and supporters. You can develop a strong list of things that others could do for you that would help you to feel better in even these most difficult times. Think back to other difficult times in your life and things that helped you then. Refer back to your list of Wellness Tools for ideas. Some of them may be very simple. Others may be harder to implement and may not always be possible but need to be included on the list just in case they are possible. Everyone's list will be different. What is helpful to one person is not necessarily helpful to someone else.

Some ideas for this list would include:
Ask me what I need, what would help.
Ask me what happened.
Let me talk and just listen to me without interrupting, judging, criticizing, correcting or advising me on what I am saying. If I want to rant and rave, let me do it as long as I am not hurting anyone or anything.
Bake me a macaroni and cheese and brownies using the attached recipe and let me eat as much of it as I want to.
Get one of the DVD's I have listed here. Make a big bowl of buttered popcorn and hot chocolate and then watch the video with me.
Encourage me to use my art supplies to draw and paint. Help me get them out and get started if you need to.
Play me one of my favorite CD's.
Take me for a long walk in the park if I am willing to go.

Bring your dog or cat over for me to play with.

Let me pace as much as I need to.

Let me punch a pillow as much as I want to.

Hold me, if I ask you to, for as long as I want to be held.

Let me cry and cry and cry.

Make sure the bathroom is safe but let me go to the bathroom when I need to.

Encourage me to wear something I really enjoy wearing — my hot pink sweater.

Stay with me in a comfortable room where I can't hurt myself.

If possible, get me some time in a hot tub.

Give me one additional dose of _____ every four hours if I ask for it, following the directions on the bottle.

The next part of this section is very important. Make a clear list of things you do <u>not</u> want people to do when you are having a hard time. Include things that people have done in the past that were not helpful and may have impeded your recovery. Again, talking with friends and supporters may give you more ideas for this list. But as always, what you include on this list is up to you. Some ideas might include:

Do not restrain me using four or five point restraints.

Do not leave me alone in an isolation or seclusion room.

Do not medicate me against my will unless it is necessary to save my life and protect others.

Don't lecture me.

Don't criticize, judge or threaten me.

Don't yell at me.

Don't disagree, even if you know that what I am saying is incorrect.

Don't touch me.

Don't laugh at me, make fun of me or try to joke with me.

Don't minimize what I am feeling.

Don't tell me you know how I feel.

Don't insist that I take a hot bath.

Don't remind me of all my failures and mistakes.

Don't threaten me with long-term hospitalization.

Don't tell the doctor not to pay any attention to my plan.

Don't shout at me.

Don't push me around.

Section 9. Chores that need to be taken care of

Include a list of tasks you need others to take care of until you feel better like:
- buying groceries
- watering the plants
- feeding the pets
- taking care of the children
- paying the bills
- taking out the garbage or trash
- doing the laundry

Make clear plans for children, elderly or ill people and pets that are dependent on your care. For instance, if you are a single parent with minor children, you need a carefully devised plan that will ensure that the children are not placed in state custody if you need hospital treatment or need to be out of the home for a time. Identify at least three people or families that the children could stay with, people that the children know well and feel comfortable with, and who agree to take on this responsibility if needed. You need three options in case one or two of the people or families is not available for some reason (sickness, out of town, work responsibilities, etc.). Make sure this is acceptable to these people. The children could either go to their home or the person or people could come and stay in your home, depending on what seems best to you and them. If you have to arrange this at the time of the crisis it will be very difficult. The state, not knowing what else to do, might step in and take over, moving your child or children to a foster home. Then it may be difficult for you to get them back when you have recovered. This would be traumatic for you and the children.

If you have dependent adults in your care, you need to set up a similar protocol for them, making sure there is a place where they can be taken to be cared for, or people who can come to your home to provide them with care. In a worst case scenario, a person could be left on their own who does not have the ability to care for him or herself. The effects could be devastating.

If you have pets, they also need to be considered in your plan. Some pets like cats and guinea pigs can easily stay at home with someone coming by every day to feed and care for them. Dogs have greater needs and usually benefit from staying with someone else for the time.

Section 10. When the crisis plan is no longer needed

Describe for your supporters how they can recognize when you have recovered enough so that you can take care of yourself and to let them know that they no longer need to use this plan.

Of course you don't want people caring for you when you can easily take care of yourself. List those signs that would tell others that you are feeling much better and that they no longer need to follow the directions in this Crisis Plan. Make sure it is clear, as you would not want someone to stop caring for you when you still need care, but would want them to stop if you were feeling much better. These statements need to be clear and precise so your supporters will know when they can step back.

Signs on this list might include:
- when I am eating at least two meals a day
- when I am awake for six hours a day
- when I am taking care of my personal hygiene needs daily
- when I can carry on a good conversation
- when I can easily walk around the house

You may want to ask your family members, friends and supporters for suggestions for this list.

Finalizing and using the plan

Now you have completed your Crisis Plan or Advance Directive. Review it and ask your supporters to review it several times before you finalize it. Have a discussion with your supporters. Ask them if there are parts of the plan that they don't understand, that could be stated more clearly, that might be hard to follow or that they think should not be included. Take their suggestions into consideration as you finalize your plan.

When you are satisfied with your plan, depending on the regulations in your state, you may want to:
- appoint a Durable Power of Attorney who is responsible for your personal business if you are in a crisis (list that person on the plan)
- sign it in the presence of two witnesses
- have it notarized
- ask a lawyer about other steps you can take to help assure that your Advance Directive will be honored

If your Advance Directive is stored on a computer, you may need to make a paper copy to get your signatures. Ask your state protection and advocacy office for information on legalizing your plan. You may also be able to get this information from a doctor, case manager, counselor, your peers, a peer organization or a mental health agency or organization.

The legality of Crisis Plans and Advance Directives varies from state to state. You cannot be absolutely sure the plan will be followed. However, it is your best assurance that your wishes will be honored. And with a strong support team that knows your plan well, you may avoid any legal issues.

You have now completed your Crisis Plan. Give copies of it to each of the people on your list of supporters, or tell them how they can easily access it online (make sure they have the capacity to do that). If they don't have on-line access, give them a paper copy each time you update your plan.

Update the plan, either online or on your paper copies, when you learn new information or change your mind about things, dating the plan each time you make a change, and notifying your supporters of these changes, giving revised hard copies of the plan to your supporters.

You may want to have a meeting of your supporters to discuss your plan and so the supporters know each other in advance.

Celebration

Completing your Advance Directive is a huge accomplishment. Celebrate in some way. Do something you love to do that is good for you and good for others. Check your list of Wellness Tools for ideas. Consider:

    Inviting friends to your home for a potluck lunch or dinner
    Taking a friend out to lunch
    Hosting a small party in your honor
    Taking a day off from your responsibilities and do only things you love to do

Now that you have completed this intensive document there are two things you can do:

To help assure that you will never need to use your Crisis Plan or Advance Directive, if you haven't already, develop and use a WRAP® Plan as described in this section of this book and in other resources you can access through www.mentalhealthrecovery.com.

In addition, prepare yourself for the possibility that you may have a crisis and review the Post Crisis Plan document that is in the next chapter of this book.

Crisis Plan/Advance Directive

Name _____ **Date** _____

Part 1 What I am like when I'm feeling well

_____

_____

_____

_____

Part 2 Indicators that I need assistance from others

If I have several of the following indicators, my supporters as named in this document need to take over responsibility for my care and make decisions on my behalf based on the information in this plan.

_____

_____

_____

_____

_____

_____

_____

_____

Part 3 Who takes over and who doesn't

If this plan needs to be activated, I want the following people to take over for me.

Name   **Connection/role**   **Phone number**

_____

Specific Tasks for this Person

_____

Name   **Connection/role**   **Phone number**

_____

Specific Tasks for this Person

_____

Name   **Connection/role**   **Phone number**

_____

Specific Tasks for this Person

_____

_____

Name	Connection/role	Phone number

Specific Tasks for this Person

I do not want the following people involved in any way in my care or treatment:

Name   **I don't want them involved because: (optional)**

Name   **I don't want them involved because: (optional)**

Name   **I don't want them involved because: (optional)**

Name   **I don't want them involved because: (optional)**

Settling Disputes Between Supporters

If my supporters disagree on a course of action to be followed, I would like the dispute to be settled in the following way:

Part 4 Medications that help and those that don't

Physician _____ **Psychiatrist** _____

Other Health Care Providers

_____

_____

_____

_____

Pharmacy _____ **Pharmacist** _____

Allergies _____

Insurance Information _____

Medications and other health care products I am currently using

Medication /Health Care Product   **Dosage**

Purpose

_____

Medication /Health Care Product   **Dosage**

_____

Purpose

_____

Medication /Health Care Product   **Dosage**

_____

Purpose

_____

Medication /Health Care Product   **Dosage**

_____

Purpose

_____

Medications and health care products that might help and why

_____

_____

_____

_____

Medications and health care products to avoid and why

_____

_____

_____

_____

Part 5 Treatments that help and those that don't

Treatments that help

_____

_____

_____

_____

Treatments to avoid

_____

_____

_____

Part 6 Home Care / Community Care / Respite Care Plan

_____

_____

_____

_____

_____

_____

_____

_____

_____

Part 7 Acceptable and unacceptable treatment facilities

If I need hospitalization or treatment in a treatment facility, I prefer the following facilities in order of preference

Name   **Contact Person**   **Phone Number**

_____

I prefer this facility because

_____

Name   **Contact Person**   **Phone Number**

_____

I prefer this facility because

_____

Name   **Contact Person**   **Phone Number**

_____

I prefer this facility because

_____

Avoid using the following hospital or treatment facilities

Name   **Reason to avoid using**

_____

_____

_____

_____

Part 8 Things that others can do that would help and things that won't help

Things that others can do that would help

_____
_____
_____
_____
_____
_____

Do not do the following. It won't help and it may even make things worse.

_____
_____
_____
_____
_____
_____
_____

Part 9 Chores I need others to take care of

_____
_____
_____
_____

Part 10 When the Crisis Plan is No Longer Needed _____

_____
_____
_____
_____
_____
_____

I developed this plan on (date) _____ with the help of _____
Any plan with a more recent date supersedes this one.

Signed _____ Date _____

Witness _____ Date _____

Witness _____ Date _____

Attorney _____ Date _____

Durable Power of Attorney _____

Substitute for Durable Power of Attorney _____

Any Personal Crisis Plan developed on a date after the dates listed above takes precedence over this document.

WRAP®

Post-Crisis Planning

The Post Crisis Plan was added to WRAP® several years after the previous sections were developed. The need for such a section was brought to my attention by Richard Hart, a Mental Health Recovery Facilitator from West Virginia. A group he was leading brought up the issue of healing after a crisis.

Post Crisis Planning seemed to complete a wellness cycle which was not quite complete with the original WRAP®. That cycle begins with wellness (Daily Maintenance Plan), moving on to Triggers, Early Warning Signs, When Things are Breaking Down and Crisis Planning. Richard and his group felt that an action plan was needed to bridge the gap between the crisis and wellness. Others agreed. And so, working with people who have a lived experience of mental health difficulties and checking it out with many others, the Post Crisis Plan became reality.

Many years ago, long before WRAP was developed, I experienced a long term, deep depression. I was hospitalized several times. The hospitalizations were somewhat helpful. I was introduced to some wellness tools, although that is not what they were called at that time, things like stress reduction and relaxation techniques and journaling. I got some peer support that I enjoyed. It helped to know I was not alone. I was stabilized on a medication regime. But the hospital experience did nothing to bridge the gap between the crisis that brought me to the hospital, my return home and my recovery. In fact, recovery was not even mentioned as a possibility.

Twice, I returned to the hospital within two days of my discharge. Why? When I got home all my family and friends considered that I must be well. I was dropped off at my apartment and spent the next few very trying hours alone. One time a friend who had promised to be there decided I must be napping, and didn't bother to call or come. There was no food. The space was messy and disorganized. I immediately felt overwhelmed and totally discouraged. In addition, there was a message that my employer expected me back at work full time in the next few days.

No matter how you work your way out of a crisis, in a hospital, in respite, in the community, or at home, you may also find that your healing takes a few steps backwards unless the journey out of this very hard place is given careful attention. I have come to believe that, for most people, it takes as long to recover from a mental health crisis as it would to recover from any other major illness or surgery. You need assistance and support that can be gradually reduced as you feel better and better.

The post crisis plan is different from other parts of WRAP®. While I encourage you to review it carefully and provide information where you can, most of this plan will be developed as you are working your way out of the crisis, as you begin to feel better. You will develop it gradually over time, perhaps with input from your care providers.

I suggest you make several copies of the Post Crisis Plan and have it easily accessible for whenever you might need it.

Working on the Post Crisis Plan

The Post Crisis Plan begins by asking you how you would like to feel when you are well. This can be the same, or different, from the descriptions in your Daily Maintenance Plan and at the beginning of your Crisis Plan. After a crisis, your perspective on wellness may have changed.

Then, like the Crisis Plan or Advance Directive, it asks you to name the supporters you want to assist you as you recover and what you would like them to do. It gives space for phone numbers. It is a good idea to list phone numbers so you can easily contact supporters from wherever you are. Get a cell phone number if that seems right. E-mail addresses might be helpful as well. Sometimes I find that when I am not feeling up to par, I would rather send an e-mail than call someone.

Hopefully, you will be able to stay at home when you are dealing with a crisis. But if you can't, plan your trip home and the conditions when you arrive home carefully. This is a very important time. You may feel quite fragile as you make this transition. That is to be expected. Think carefully about who you want to take you home, who you want to stay with you when you get home, what you want to do when you get there and those things that would be helpful to you during your first few hours, things you can ask supporters to do in advance. That list might include tidying up, doing the laundry, getting groceries, and picking up your dog so it can be there when you arrive. This is a time to be gentle with yourself. Put off any unpleasant task that you must do until you have had time to get used to being home.

Develop a complete list of things to do for yourself every day while you are recovering. Your Daily Maintenance List and your list of Things You Might Need to Do can guide you as you work on this.This will give you ideas but the lists may not be exactly the same. Include a strong list of things and people you want to avoid as you are recovering. For instance, you may want to avoid your computer, the evening news, your brother and a particular peer.

The section that asks you to list signs that you are beginning to feel worse is very important.

You will need to be in touch with how you feel and respond quickly to any signs that you are beginning to feel worse.

My overwhelming loneliness when I was alone was a sign for me that I needed to do something to help myself instead of allowing myself to feel worse and worse. Calling a special friend and asking them to come over might be on your list. Or there may be a particular television show or some music that would help you feel better. Perhaps reading a good book or taking a walk would help.

As you are feeling better, there will be particular issues you want to address to prevent further repercussions from this crisis. For instance, you may want to call your employer and tell her or him how you are doing and when you think you might return to work. You may need to pay your rent or talk to your landlord about why your payment was late. You may want to reconnect with a special friend.

Spend some time thinking about who you need to thank. My supporters are always at the top of my list. I always thank them in person whenever I can. But a phone call is nice as well. An e-mail is not as personal. It is great if, as you are feeling better, you can do something nice for them, like take them to lunch, bake them some cookies or invite them to your home for popcorn and a movie.

It helps to relieve stress if you take care of apologies and making amends with people you may have offended as quickly as possible. It will also help to relieve stress if you can quickly take care of medical, legal, or financial issues that need to be resolved, and doing what you can to prevent further loss. Hopefully you have some good supporters who can help you with this hard work. Do it a bit at a time so it doesn't overwhelm you. Your recovery is most important. Be gentle with yourself.

Timetable for Resuming Responsibilities

The next section is a timetable for resuming your responsibilities. When you were unable to care for yourself, others may have had to take over responsibility for some of the things you usually do. Resuming these responsibilities all at once could be a disaster. Gradually resuming them over time is often the best choice. A worksheet is included with the plan to make this process easier for you.

Other issues I may want to consider

As you finish working on your Post Crisis Plan and either putting it away until you want to work on it some more, or putting it into action when you need to, you may want to think about signs that would let you know that this post crisis phase is over and you can return to using your Daily Maintenance Plan as your guide to wellness and recovery. For instance, you might feel you are ready to move out of this Post Crisis phase when you have gone back to work, are taking care of your children and pets, are cooking yourself dinner or you are able to sleep 6 hours at night.

This is a good time to review your Advance Directive/Crisis Plan and decide if there are some changes that you want to make in the Plan so that it works better for you another time. For instance you might decide one of your supporters was not helpful, you may want to add another supporter who might be more helpful, you might want to avoid a certain hospital or medication, you may have discovered that riding an exercise bike for half an hour a day helps you a lot, and that when you eat sugar you feel more anxious.

You also may decide to make some changes in your Wellness Recovery Action Plan as a result of what you learned in this hard time. For instance, you may want to add yoga that you learned at the respite center as a Wellness Tool, you may want to add checking in with a supporter to your Daily Maintenance List, and you may want to add being yelled at and being threatened with hospitalization to your list of Triggers.

In a crisis, people often do a lot of "soul searching." When they are feeling better they may decide to make a major change in their lifestyle or their goals, based on what they have learned. For instance, you may decide to:
> Change careers
> Move to a different town or location (city to country)
> Get more education

A crisis can often be a time of great learning. It may help you to do some journaling about what you learned in this crisis. You may decide there are changes you want to make in your life as a result of what you have learned. Writing the specifics of how you plan to make these changes can help to bring them to fruition. Some changes you might decide to make might include:
> Move into supported housing
> End a close relationship
> Avoid certain people
> Stay away from certain places
> Change careers
> Go back to school
> Lose weight
> Stop smoking

Use the following form to complete your post crisis plan. If you are using a binder, write *"Post Crisis Plan"* on a tab and insert the form. Or use the copy in the computer program or the Build Your Own WRAP e-learning course.

Perspectives On Post Crisis Planning by Richard Hart

Richard Hart of West Virginia, a Mental Health Recovery Educator, brought the concept of Post Crisis Planning to my attention. He shared the insights that follow.

Returning to your everyday, healthy diet may require some assistance. A trip to the grocery store is often a task that must be undertaken the first day home. One person told me that after the strict regime of hospital food, when they went to the supermarket, all they could do was fill the cart with "junk." Sugar, salt, fat, those foods that were restricted when meals were prepared and snacks were monitored by a nutritionist, became the attractive "forbidden fruit." The same thing happened with alcohol. This particular person, a very moderate social drinker, wound up with a hangover the first morning they woke up in their own bed. Be certain that good food is available when you come home. Don't be afraid to indulge in any of you favorites, even if they be "guilty pleasures." Just don't go overboard.

People who are returning to a family have a different set of concerns. As much as we would and do, miss our children, depending on the individual circumstance, we may need some help initially resuming our parenting duties. As with those who return to the workplace, a gradual resumption may be best. Some children may enjoy a visit with another family member; older children may enjoy spending some time at a friend's house. No matter what, the dynamics of returning to family life present concerns that must be anticipated in order to cope with potential difficulties.

As with all the elements of WRAP®, a post crisis plan is very individualized. One of the most important considerations is whether or not an individual is living alone. Those of us who live alone have very different concerns than those of us who do not. Making certain that I have a friend stay with me at least the first night I am back home is most important to me and others in my situation. In discussing whether or not one might stay with a friend, we felt it was better to be back in one's own space. However, that first day alone again can be most difficult. After the first day back, one can make a decision as to whether or not additional companioning is needed.

Sometimes, one may not be able to make arrangements to have someone stay with you. Coming home to a comfortable, clean home is in that case most important.

Folks who discussed this all agreed that many of us have come home to a house that was most unkempt. Exposure to that can bring on distressing memory of our days when "things were breaking down." Arrangements to have a friend straighten up, or hiring someone, can make a big difference. I suggest that people find a good time to clean a friend's house so that it will be the return of a favor, rather than asking someone to do the housework that is a chore to anyone.

Who would think that the mail could be traumatizing? It can. Having a trusted supporter go through one's mail before we do can shield us from distressing overdue notices and the like. I have found that making out a check is no problem, but reading those awful "PAY NOW OR DIE" notes from a creditor is rough.

Spreading the word to friends and associates that one is "back" is a task that can be a bit daunting to someone in the early stages of recovery. A buddy can be enlisted to call folks to let them know how you are and also let them know if you would like them to visit or call. Some folks may welcome visits, while others would prefer some time to "decompress" before seeing friends. The same is true for phone calls.

Along the same line, reentering the workplace should be thought out carefully. Personally, I have made the mistake of trying to go back to work too quickly. I have found that for me a gradual re-entry is best. Working a few hours for a few days has been good for me.

Finally, after you have readapted to everyday life, your WRAP plan needs to be revisited. Any crisis we endure will show us something new about the prevention of another. You may want to enlist the aid of therapist, supporter, and family to examine what can be learned from the experience. Determine if new triggers have been discovered. Talk about early warning signs that may have been unnoticed. Think about additions to the daily maintenance plan. Sharpen the wellness tools you already have and see if new ones will be helpful. Perhaps most importantly, scrutinize the plan for when things are breaking down. Determine what can be done in the future to prevent further crisis. Be especially sensitive to critical signs that may have been ignored or missed. Finally, ascertain the effectiveness of your crisis plan.

POST CRISIS PLAN

How I would like to feel when I have recovered from this crisis

You may want to refer to the first section of your Wellness Recovery Action Plan — What I am Like When I am Well. What you write here may be different from what you have listed before for what you feel like when you are well — your perspective may have changed in this crisis.

_____

_____

Post Recovery Supporters List

I would like the following people to support me if possible during this post crisis time.

Who   Phone number   What I need them to do

_____   _____   _____

_____   _____   _____

_____   _____   _____

_____   _____   _____

_____   _____   _____

_____   _____   _____

Arriving at Home

If you have been hospitalized, your first few hours at home are very important.

I would like _____ or _____ to take me home.

I would like _____ or _____ stay with me.

When I get home I would like to _____ or _____.

If the following things are in place, it would ease my return:

_____

_____

_____

Things I must take care of as soon as I get home

_____

_____

_____

Things I can ask someone else to do for me

_____

_____

_____

Things that can wait until I feel better

_____

_____

_____

Things I need to do for myself every day while I am recovering from crisis

_____

_____

_____

_____

_____

_____

_____

Things I might need to do every day while I am recovering from this crisis

_____

_____

_____

Things and people I need to avoid while I am recovering from this crisis

_____

_____

_____

Signs that I may be beginning to feel worse — anxiety, excessive worry, overeating, sleep disturbances

_____

_____

_____

Wellness tools I will use if I am starting to feel worse — star those that you must do — the others are choices

_____

_____

_____

Issues to consider

What do I need to do to prevent further repercussions from this crisis — and when I will do these things.

_____

_____

_____

_____

People I need to thank.

Person When I will thank them How I will thank them

_____
_____
_____
_____
_____

People I need to apologize to

Person When I will apologize How I will apologize

_____
_____
_____
_____

People with whom I need to make amends

Person When I will make amends How I will make amends _____

_____
_____
_____
_____

Medical, legal, or financial issues that need to be resolved

Issue How I plan to resolve this issue

_____
_____
_____
_____

Things I need to do to prevent further loss — like canceling credit cards, getting official leave from work if it was abandoned, cutting ties with destructive friends, etc.

_____
_____
_____
_____
_____

Timetable for Resuming Responsibilities

Set up a reasonable timetable for resuming responsibilities that others have taken over, things like child care, pet care, job, cooking, household chores. For example, if your responsibility is getting back to work, the steps to do that might be:

> in three days go back to work for 2 hours a day for five days
>
> for one week go back to work half time
>
> for one week work 3/4 time
>
> resume full work schedule

The following worksheet may help you with this process.

Responsibility _____ Who has been doing this while I was in crisis _____

While I am resuming this responsibility, I need (who) _____

to _____

> Plan for resuming responsibility

> _____
>
> _____
>
> _____
>
> _____

Responsibility _____ Who has been doing this while I was in crisis _____

While I am resuming this responsibility, I need (who) _____

to _____

> Plan for resuming responsibility

> _____
>
> _____
>
> _____
>
> _____

Responsibility _____ Who has been doing this while I was in crisis _____

While I am resuming this responsibility, I need (who) _____

to _____

> Plan for resuming responsibility

> _____
>
> _____
>
> _____
>
> _____

Other issues I may want to consider

Signs that this post crisis phase is over and I can return to using my Daily Maintenance Plan as my guide to things to do for myself every day.

_____
_____
_____
_____

Changes in my Wellness Recovery Action Plan that might help prevent a crisis in the future.

_____
_____
_____
_____
_____

Changes in my crisis plan that might ease my recovery.

_____
_____
_____
_____
_____

Changes I want to make in my lifestyle or life goals.

_____
_____
_____
_____
_____

What did I learn from this crisis? _____

_____
_____

Are there changes I want or need to make in my life as a result of what I have learned?

_____
_____

If so, when and how will I make these changes?

_____

_____

WRAP®

Living WRAP®

Developing WRAP is the easy part. Now comes the real WRAP challenge, using your WRAP as a daily guide to Recovery and Wellness.

Have your WRAP easily accessible. You can have it on your computer, using *Build Your Own WRAP* (www.mentalhealthrecovery.com) or *WRAP for Your Computer*. Over time I expect there will be other computer-based WRAP®applications you can use for your WRAP. You can have it in a three-ring binder, use the forms in a WRAP book or even develop a filing system with a file folder for each section. Your personal circumstances will determine what is best for you. For instance, people who are living in shelters find a pocket-sized notebook to be the best place to keep their WRAP. You may come up with other innovative ways to develop and keep your WRAP.

Have your WRAP available, where you can easily find it, and for easy review — on your computer, your breakfast table, bedside table, desk or desktop, in your briefcase, pocket or pocketbook.

At first review it every day. As you get used to it over time you will need to review it less and less. You will remember what is on your lists and what to do in varying circumstances. When things are difficult, you will probably want to go back to reviewing it more often, every day or even several times a day.

Revise your WRAP whenever you feel you need or want to. Most people revise their plan often. There are no rules around how often you should revise your plan. In fact, there are no rules about WRAP, except that you are the only one who can develop your WRAP. Only you decide what is in your WRAP and how you will use it.

Wellness Toolbox

The Wellness Toolbox is the cornerstone of developing a WRAP® and a key wellness resource. For many people, the Wellness Toolbox is their first introduction to the idea that there are simple, safe things they can do to help themselves.

In addition to using your Wellness Toolbox to build your action plans, use it on a daily basis for ideas for things to do that will help you feel better and enhance and enrich your life. Have your Wellness Toolbox easily accessible. Hang a copy on the refrigerator or on a bulletin board. Have it on your desk top. Use it for daily planning and even moment-to-moment planning.

Add new tools whenever you notice or discover them. You can get ideas on new tools from various books I have written, like *Winning Against Relapse* and *The Depression Workbook*. There are lots of other self help books that you can find at your library or bookstore that are loaded with Wellness Tools. You can find Wellness Tools on the internet. Friends, supporters and care providers are an excellent source of Wellness Tools ideas. Classes, workshops, seminars, and groups of various kinds can be a wealth of Wellness Tools.

Carry a small notebook with you. Every time you notice a Wellness Tool, jot it down. When you can, add them to your Wellness Toolbox list.

Some people have a physical box, basket or drawer where they keep certain Wellness Tools like:
> CDs and videos
> books and magazines
> art supplies
> pictures
> musical instruments
> list of other Wellness Tools

You could have a Wellness Toolbox area in your home:
> a room or part of a room
> a workshop area
> a corner or a closet

What I am Like When I am Well

The section "What I am like when I am well" is the WRAP touchstone. Refer back to it whenever you can't remember what it is like to feel really well. It keeps you on track and gives you something to work toward when you are having a difficult time.

As you get to know more about what it feels like to feel well, add words to the list. Include a picture or several pictures of yourself that you really like. Write a poem or story about yourself. Make a list of your positive attributes and achievements to include.

Daily Maintenance List

The Daily Maintenance List is the key to day-to-day wellness.
Make sure this list really works for you, that it is not too long and not too short. Revise it as needed, as you recover. Change it when it stops working for you.

Keep your days set up so it is easy to do the things on this list. Notice how much better you feel when you do the things on this list. You may want to include doing all the things on my Daily Maintenance List as a reminder on all your action plans.

Things I might need to do

When you are first using your WRAP, refer to this list every day. Not doing something on this list can get you really off track.

A good question to ask yourself in the morning: What are the things I need to do today to avoid stress in my life, to keep things going smoothly. Then do them. As you do this work on your own behalf you are becoming your own best friend.

Triggers

Over time you will become more and more aware of your triggers.

When you notice them, stop everything, think about your action plan and choose to do one or several things on that list until you feel OK again.

If something really big happens, the kind of thing you don't like to predict, use the tools listed in your action plan more intensively. Go back to your Wellness Toolbox and use other tools as well. You may need to take some time off from your responsibilities to do these things. It is worth it. It keeps you on track.

You may need a wellness afternoon, day, days or even weeks or months depending on what has happened. You work your way through difficult times using your action plan and your Wellness Tools as your guide and support. It's not easy, but it works.

Over time you will recognize your triggers more quickly. You will be able to identify more of them. Using WRAP®, some things that used to be triggers may no longer be triggers.

Early Warning Signs

Identifying and responding to your Early Warning Signs helps you to be in touch with yourself and get to know yourself very well. Over time, you will know yourself better and better and more easily recognize these signs. "Living it" means stopping when you notice these signs, and doing the things on your action plan. It may mean three 5-minute breaks, a long talk with a friend, canceling an event, avoiding someone or something — whatever works for you.

When Things are Breaking Down

When things are breaking down is a critical time. You feel awful, horrific. It is the hardest time to take care of yourself. It may be the time when, in the past, others stepped in and took care of you. Perhaps you were even hospitalized.

Using WRAP® and your Wellness Tools, you can bring yourself back to a place of wellness. It takes perseverance. But **YOU CAN DO IT.**

This section needs to be strong, clear and directive. Keep revising it so it works well for you. It may include "hospital days" at home. I suggest you develop several plans for hospital days at home as Wellness Tools and keep them in your binder. Do this by making a plan for everything you will do through the day with times, For example, 7 am get up, shower, dress, 7:30 make myself cereal and toast for breakfast and eat it, 8 am, call and talk to my sister, 8:30 am, work on my quilting project, 9:30 am, reading, 10:30 am, take the dog for a walk, and so on.

Once you have developed these plans, I suggest you try them out. Choose a day and follow the directions on your plan exactly. See how it works. This can help you to identify and work out any possible flaws in your plan.

Support is key at this time. You are worth it.

Crisis Plan or Advance Directive

As part of Living WRAP, you need to develop and give your supporters copies of your Crisis Plan/ Advance Directive. For ease of updating and access, you could have it online in the Build Your Own WRAP Program. Then your supporters would need to know your password. Or you can give each person paper copies, giving them new copies when you revise your plan.

The hope is that you will never need to use your plan. Now that more and more people are using WRAP®, they are reporting that they have fewer or no "crisis times." But as the old saying goes, "It is better to be safe than sorry."

Your Crisis Plan/Advance Directive is different from other part of your plan, in that you have to write it so others can use it. They need to be able to understand what you are saying. I suggest that when you give it to them, you read it over together. Then they can ask you questions about any parts they don't understand.

Some parts of the plan are easy to develop, like your list of medications and care providers.

The sections I feel need lots of attention, to ensure that they will work for you, are:
1. The list of signs that others need to step in and take care of you. Like most of us, you may have had times when others stepped in when you didn't really need their help, and they took action on your behalf that was not helpful or was even harmful.

2. A clear list of who you want, and who you don't want involved in your care.

3. A detailed plan that tells others <u>exactly</u> how they can provide care for you at home or in the community.

4. Things that others can do for you that help, and things others should not do.

5. A clear list of indicators that supporters can stop using this plan.

Post Crisis Plan

Take the time to carefully consider in advance that time when you are healing from a crisis. Review all of the questions in advance. Jot down any notes that you think might be helpful to you. Talk with your supporters about it.

When you healing from a crisis, you may feel ready to begin taking care of yourself again. But you may still be dealing with upsetting feelings and the aftermath of the crisis. You may find that you start feeling worse — like you are heading for another crisis. "Living WRAP" at this time is especially challenging.

Thinking about this time, before you even have a crisis, and giving it more attention when you are starting to feel better after a crisis, may help you have an easier time recovering and moving on.

WRAP Day to Day

At first you may want to review your plan every day, follow your Daily Maintenance Plan, and take other action as needed.
After a while you will notice that you remember your plan and only need to refer to it from time to time, unless you are having a difficult time.

Revise your plan when you discover new Wellness Tools and find that some things work better for you than others, and as the circumstances of your life change.

LIVING WRAP Resources

There are resources you can use to assist and support you in Living WRAP. They include but are not limited to:

    Talking to others who have had similar experiences
    Joining a WRAP support group
    The Websites: mentalhealthrecovery.com, wraparoundtheworld.com, copleandcenter.com
    Mental Health Recovery and WRA® newsletter and other mental health newsletters
    Build Your Own Wrap Online
    Creating a Wellness Toolbox, WRAP One on One and other online mental health recovery and WRAP courses
    Books, audios, videos including:

        The WRAP Story
        Winning Against Relapse
        The Depression Workbook
        WRAP books

If I had my life to live over

Years ago, when deep depressions and other mental health challenges were a way of life for me, my only options seemed to be medical treatment and hospitalization. I was actually relieved when I was told that there was a pill, Lithium, which along with an anti-depressant, might give me lots of relief. Here was something I could easily do, and it would fix everything.
I had a lot of difficult issues in my life at that time that were not addressed an abusive and unsupportive spouse, five adolescent children and various foster children that I was responsible

for, and running a school for children with learning and emotional difficulties.

I never took time off, I didn't have any rest or relaxation, I never bought anything nice for myself, I never even went out to eat or to a movie, I didn't have time for friends, my self-esteem was in the cellar and I had unresolved trauma issues from my childhood.

I bought the medication and I started taking it. I took it for a very long time, until I had a toxic reaction to it when I had a stomach "bug." I got very, very sick. And that was the end of that. My body didn't want lithium anymore.

But still I didn't get it. With my doctor's help, I began a long search for other drugs that would replace the lithium. And over time, both my physical and mental health deteriorated, along with the quality of my life. I remember the exact moment when I said to myself, "there has got to be a different way, and I am going to find it."

Even though I had serious brain fog by that time, working with my vocational rehabilitation counselor, I began to study how people who experience all kinds of so-called "psychiatric symptoms" cope with these intense feelings and behaviors on a daily basis, how they live their lives, how they recover and move on. I learned the most amazing things. What I learned changed my life completely, and subsequently, as I shared my findings in books, videos and trainings, changed many, many other lives.

If I had my life to live over, and if I had known then what I know now, when I first began noticing feelings of sadness, anxiety, irrational fear and worry that were getting in the way of my life, instead of going to the doctor, I would have sat down with a pencil and paper and developed a WRAP for myself. But WRAP had not even been developed at that time. But if it had.....

First I would have made a list of Wellness Tools. I think that would have been enough to get me lifted up enough to do the rest of the Plan and to get me feeling better. On my list of Wellness Tools at that time I would have included many things "not to do." They would have included:

Do not commit to doing more things in 24 hours than I can possibly do.

Do not take on any new responsibilities.

Do not neglect my own needs for food, rest and sleep.

Do not spend time with people who treat me badly (there were a few back then but not anymore).

Do not eat sugar (it makes me feel horrible).

At least once a month, buy myself something to wear that feels just right.

Just those few things would have made a huge difference for me. I would never have needed any lithium. More positive things would have been:

Buy myself something pretty (in those days I only bought things for my children).
Take a walk in the woods every day.
Take an adult education class.
Take a day off and pamper myself all day.
Spend time with good friends, people who are affirming and supportive.
Lay in the hammock and look up at the trees.

I could go on and on with lists of Wellness Tools I could have used back then. Then I would have used those tools to develop the rest of the plan. My Daily Maintenance Plan would have given me strict instructions on what to eat, when to eat it, when to go to bed and when to take some time for myself.

My abusive spouse would have been at the top of my list of triggers, and with my WRAP I think I would have gotten myself out of that situation much sooner. My Triggers Action Plan would have said "Avoid people who treat you badly," and that would have been the end of that.

My Early Warning Signs would have included feeling overwhelmed, tired and worn out. Some days of rest and relaxation and asking others to take over some of my responsibilities would have easily addressed that.

When things were breaking down, like I was crying all the time, I would have had a long talk with a friend. Perhaps we would have planned a retreat together. Or I would have spent a whole afternoon working in my garden, hiking in the hills or working on a quilt.

I would have developed an intensive crisis plan for myself. Probably I would never have needed it. But if I did, it would have been there to tell others how to provide me with care until I could again care for myself.

Here I am now, all these years later. I now have a WRAP On-line that I use as my daily guide to living. I update it regularly, whenever I feel the need.

Every day I need and use my WRAP. Today I have had some bad news about a colleague who is having some health challenges. My work is overwhelming. I have too much too do. Instead of reaching for the pill bottle (I don't have a stash anymore) I am thinking of fixing myself a healthy snack and eating it on the back porch where I can listen to the birds. Then I will work in my garden for a bit and call a friend for a supportive chat. I will cook myself a healthy dinner and eat with my spouse. I will stay home this evening and take a short walk, finish reading that good book that I picked up last week at the library, and get a good night's sleep.

I am strongly reminded of the importance of "Living WRAP" every single day. There is a lot of unexpected and serious illness in my family. Every day my family's welfare is my primary concern. As I age, I have some health issues that need attention as well. And maintaining my mental health needs my attention every single day. Now I can really say that I am "Living WRAP," not day to day, but moment to moment.

Every single moment I have to think about my Daily Maintenance Plan. I ask myself, "What do I have to do today for myself to be sure I can be available to others if needed?" Then I have to be absolutely sure I do those things.

Often I get a call with a new piece of information or find myself waiting and waiting for reassurance that all is well. I now have first-hand experience with how to get by, using my Triggers Action Plan, as I wait and wait and wait. It is not easy but I have managed. I keep reminding myself that if I "fall apart," it is not going to help anybody and it will make it more difficult for everybody. So I pick up my knitting, find a diversionary TV program or watch a video, clean something that really needs it, talk to my spouse, read something or use one of the other tools in my Triggers Action Plan to get me through the long hard hours and even days.

Being ever watchful, there are times when I notice Early Warning Signs creeping in. Then I refer to that action plan, and intensify my efforts at maintaining my wellness, to get myself back on track as quickly as possible.

And there are times when, if I wasn't paying close attention, I could easily find myself in the "When things are breaking down" section of my WRAP. Early this morning I talked with a friend about a child sexual abuse case we are both working on. When I got off the phone, I would have easily fit into this category, so deep was my despair and my concern for this small child. I needed quick evasive action. So I had a talk with my spouse, went to a yoga class at the senior center, had tea and a loving chat with a dear friend, took a long walk in the woods, and had a healthy dinner. This was so different from the old days, when deep despair would have meant popping extra pills, canceling activities and maybe a trip to the emergency room or the hospital.

I also want to mention the importance to me of having a strong Wellness Toolbox that is constantly revised as I uncover new Wellness Tools. Whenever I get into a real "pinch', where things are really hard and my action plans don't seem to be doing it, I get out my Wellness Toolbox, which now contains over 100 possible options, and so far, I have always found something I could do that would help.

Sometimes I find it helpful in "Living WRAP" to review some of what I have written, and what others have written about WRAP, in my books, and on the websites (www.mentalhealthrecovery. com, www.wraparoundthe world.com). I Particularly recommend The WRAP Story, a collection of WRAP stories from WRAP users all over the world.

Problem Solving Activity

At the end of the WRAP® Group Facilitator Training, participants are led through an activity that helps them to think more broadly about possible solutions in any situation. In the training, a piece of newsprint paper is taped to the wall. A participant shares a problem that they have, or anticipate, in working with a group. Then group members share ideas for how the problem might be resolved. There are usually 10 or 12 possibilities listed. Then the newsprint sheet is given to the person with the problem, so they can choose which solution or solutions to use. Invariably one or more of the solutions will work. You can use a similar activity, on your own or with your supporters, coming up with possible solutions that will work for you, and then deciding the best one or ones to use.

All through my day, I come up with problems and issues that I need to resolve, issues that have to do with my mental health. Things like, "I am feeling tired and fragile this afternoon." What should I do? My solutions are in my WRAP. Usually I go through it in my head, as I have used it so much I don't even need to look at it. Tired and fragile. Those are Early Warning Signs. What are things on my Early Warning Signs Action Plan that I need to do? Are there other things in my Wellness Toolbox that might help? Using this method, problem solving and taking action right away, I quickly address and resolve the problem. Because of WRAP, I have many, many possible solutions.

WRAP Stories

Following are several stories by people who live WRAP. I have not edited them nor judged the content since I cannot know what might be helpful and meaningful to you.

Steven Wilkinson writes:

I didn't know anything about WRAP until about 4 years ago, when I was diagnosed, and was surprised how it started to work in my life, with my mental conditions, to assist me along with my medication that I am taking. This WRAP program helps me recognize when things start to go wrong and the things that I can do to recover. I also use it for my job. I am in the mental health field, and it helps me every day to handle days when they are not "take me away Calgon" days.

Sometimes, my job can be really stressful, and all I have to do is work my WRAP by going back, and learn to go to my happy place, and relax and compose myself, to get me through the day. Last but not least, I help the clients learn how they can handle life's ups and downs by having a conversation with them on WRAP (things they like to do, how to cope when things start going wrong and what they can do to remain stable etc.). I must say that WRAP has made me realize the strengths and weakness about myself and get to know more about who I am.

Beth Mosier writes:

I was diagnosed with major depression years ago when I was a young mother with four small children. I was introduced to the WRAP when I worked as a case manager here in Kansas. It really struck me as a tool I could benefit from to manage my symptoms, especially in light of the fact that I was unable to take therapeutic doses of the needed antidepressants, because of a horrible sensitivity/allergy to them. I went through the initial 2-day training with a client, but then took the WRAP and developed my own plan. I have used it and revised it for years now, so that I can monitor my own symptoms and be more in tune to what kind of space I'm in. When I went back to work after an especially difficult relapse of symptoms, I developed a simple plan to apply at work. I chose several support people and provided them with a copy of my plan. I also gave a copy to my supervisor. Until I could more consistently recognize my own symptoms, my supporters would refer to my plan to help me recognize what I was feeling and what I needed to do for myself. Now, I am able to use the plan myself. I still have support people, but I don't need to have them point out my symptoms anymore because now I recognize them myself. I use the plan to help me know what kind of self-care to give myself, and to know when I need to take a day off, adjust my work schedule, or touch base with someone. I keep a list of daily maintenance cues in my office where I can see it every day, to remind me of the most simple things I need to do: open my office door so I don't isolate, touch base with a supportive person, tell someone how I am feeling, tell my supervisor if I'm feeling overwhelmed, and ask for help prioritizing my work tasks.

I love the WRAP and now, as a training specialist, I have incorporated WRAP® training as part of the training for new case managers and I encourage all of them to use this great tool with the people they work with!

Ken Braiterman writes:

When I'm having my normal reaction to a trigger, or severe trigger, I say I've been triggered or re-traumatized, or experiencing difficulty, not "getting sick." Post-traumatic stress issues are not a disease; they're normal human reactions to an abnormal event that really happened. Those bad, even suicidal, feelings go away, if you don't kill yourself first. From WRAP, I've learned dozens of ways to keep postponing the suicide attempt until the feelings go away. Only once in the past 30 years have I had a suicidal siege that took two days to overcome. 30 years ago, I postponed for four days, and was really isolated and alone. I'm not alone now. I have plenty of help. I talk back to the bad (not suicidal) feelings, and do other things to make them go away faster, or just take my mind off my mind. I know the nasty voices are lying to me, because I know I'm a good, worthwhile person who has done a lot of good for a lot of people. I used to keep a list of my accomplishments handy, but I remember them now, and haven't needed a written list for a long time. I write every day, but not the journal writing that turns my mind inward. I always write for a reader, even if it's an e-mail. So I have to make it interesting and readable for somebody else. That turns my mind outward. A bad back limits my ability to exercise, but I take walks and do floor exercises to help my back. Exercise is still "the best anti-depressant, and it's free," as WRAP® says. My favorite diversionary activity is watching old movies on TV. And if I'm able to concentrate, I read non-fiction. I don't make projects or do household chores. They help a lot of people, but drive me crazy. I do keep the kitchen neat, and that makes me feel less depressed. I call my supporters, one in particular, because we have a uniquely equal, mutual peer support relationship, and others if she's not available, and I can't wait until she is. But the most important thing for me is not being scared of my own mind. "This too shall pass," and "What doesn't kill you makes you strong."

D. Gen Derrick writes:

WRAP, for me, begins as I wake in the morning. If I take a shower, I know I will feel better about myself and be ready for the day. If I can make my bed before work, that is a bonus. To me, it is about feeling good about myself. I take my medications as I leave the house too. By keeping them all in one place, I don't forget to take them. That used to be a problem, a medicine bottle here, a medicine bottle there. Did I take that pill? Now it is not a problem because I have them all together.

When I drive to work, I smile and think about the people I am going to help. I will probably learn more from them than they will from me. I am a case manager/certified peer counselor. I make sure I say hi to all the staff that is there, for I do not know if they are taking care of themselves like I am with my WRAP. My desk has hope statements, figurines and pictures that are a part of my toolbox, right on my desk. I believe that hope is where recovery begins and I am privileged to share it with my co-workers and clients throughout the day.

I do share WRAP with my clients, and emphasize to them about support. We talk about places they can get it, and be able to have it even if the mental health center is closed. I talk to them about groups and try to help them find one they are interested in. Once in a group for a while they understand there are group dynamics that one cannot get anywhere else. It is powerful. These are the clients that not only survive, but they thrive.

One day I was supposed to do my usual weekly support group for people one step out of a mental hospital, either way. On the short drive there, I began to realize that this was the first year I was not going to have my mom on Mother's Day. She died a few months ago. I started to cry and thought to myself, "I can't do group if I am the leader and here I am crying as I walk in the door." But, I thought about my WRAP and what I should do. I should go into that group and do what I do best, tell what it is like to have a mental illness like them. I knew the group was going to help me that day more than the clients knew. As each member shares (they change every week), I shared this week about my mom. I shared from my heart. I cried, laughed and the others were problem-solving for me. It was incredible. When I had first walked into the group, no one thought I had a problem in the world. In the hour I spent with these five great people, they were helping each other and themselves about what triggers them and what to do about it. WRAP has changed my life forever. My dream is that one day all clients and family/friends know about WRAP.

Wellness and Recovery Strategies

Medical Considerations

Mental health challenges were, for many years, an overwhelming part of my life. I assumed I had had a complete medical check-up because of numerous hospitalizations. When I was referred to an endocrinologist and treated for hypothyroidism, my mind cleared and I felt much, much better. With proper treatment of the thyroid disorder and using a variety of self-help strategies, I finally have my life back.

Many people who have mental health challenges have found that they have medical conditions that must be treated in order to achieve their personal optimal level of wellness. Treatment for some disorders eliminates the troubling symptoms. I found that, with treatment for the medical problems, I felt somewhat better. That made it easier for me to address the remaining mental health challenges I had in other ways. These difficulties are disruptive and detrimental to your quality of life, your ability to responsibly take care of yourself, and your ability to fulfill your life responsibilities to family and your vocation. The expense for a thorough physical examination is absolutely warranted in every case. Hopefully, you have health care coverage that will cover these costs.

If you, or a person you support, experience any of the following, a complete comprehensive health and medical evaluation is needed right away.

1. Depression which persists longer than two weeks, or is interfering with quality of life, family, career, or other responsibilities. Sometimes depression is attributed to a major loss or life change and you will need time to heal. However, if the depression persists, the stress may have caused a physical condition which needs to be treated. Or a physical condition may have created the stress and/or depression.

2. Agitated depression (depression accompanied by desperate, repetitious movement, words and crying accompanied by feelings of anxiety, anguish and panic) or deep, suicidal depression.

3. Moods which alternate from high to low and interfere with quality of life, and career and family responsibilities.

4. Moods that include signs like bizarre and reckless behavior, flight of ideas, inability to sleep or stay still, aggression, over-commitment, and pressured speech.

5. Severe anxiety that keeps someone from doing the things they want to do and being the way they want to be.

6. Other distressing signs like hearing voices, hallucinations, paranoia and delusions.

The kinds of signs listed above can have many different causes. If underlying physical causes that need treatment are not addressed, other treatments may be ineffective, and health issues that need immediate attention may be dangerously overlooked. Medications for diagnosed illnesses like diabetes, arthritis and various gastrointestinal disorders may also create mental health challenges. Hormonal changes like puberty, perimenopause, and menopause need to be considered as well.

There are numerous accounts of people whose mental health difficulties improve dramatically when they are treated for hypothyroidism or hyperthyroidism.

• A 42 year old woman who has had mood instability for 7 years also has hormonal imbalances, endometriosis, low thyroid, and alcoholism. She says that hormonal imbalances and low thyroid obviously affect her mood. These conditions had to be cleared up before she could really work on her wellness.

• A young woman had severe agitated depression for several years that was resistant to treatment. A wide range of medications, as well as various life changes, and stress reduction techniques had been tried. Finally, a CAT scan revealed a brain tumor. Critical surgery removed the tumor, ended her depression and saved her life.

You may have felt embarrassed about going to the doctor and reporting what are commonly thought of as "psychological" or "emotional" symptoms. You may have felt that "real symptoms" have to be physical in nature, such as a broken leg or high blood pressure, that signs of mental health issues are not really sickness. You may have been afraid of a diagnosis that might indicate it was your fault you feel the way you do. You may believe that, and that if you handled things differently, you would not feel this way.

It is important to change the way you think about these issues. The medical community is acknowledging more and more that all illnesses have their physiological and psychological components. A blushing reaction is a clear example of the connection between physiological and emotional symptoms. Don't let misperceptions get in the way of appropriate treatment.

A medical evaluation begins with a careful medical history. This includes a completely honest and frank discussion of all symptoms, even those that seem irrelevant or unimportant, such as tingling sensations and digestive disturbances.

The physician chosen for this examination needs to be sensitive and compassionate to your needs, and willing to listen to, and address, your concerns. You need to feel comfortable, safe, and validated during the examination.

I have an appointment with (doctor's name) _____ on (date) _____ at (time) _____ at (address of doctor's office) _____ .

To facilitate this process, make a copy of the following form and answer the questions before your appointment. Take it with you to your physical examination. In the doctor's office, it is easy to forget to share information that may be vital to the physician's search for answers.

Information for the Physician

1. All medications, vitamins and health care preparations you are using for any reason.

Medication	Dosage	When and How Used
_____	_____	_____
_____	_____	_____
_____	_____	_____
_____	_____	_____
_____	_____	_____
_____	_____	_____

2. A medical history of yourself and your family (review the list at the end of this section to assist your recall). You may remember your mother talking about her thyroid disorder, or Uncle Jake talking about his diabetes. Review the list with one or several family members who may have some valuable input. Look the list over several times in case there is something you have overlooked.

Mother's side of the Family

_____
_____
_____
_____

Father's side of the Family

_____
_____
_____
_____

3. Describe changes in:

appetite or diet _____

weight _____

sleep patterns _____

sexual interest _____

ability to concentrate _____

memory _____

bowel and urinary habits _____

4. If you have recently had any of the following symptoms, describe them:

_____ headaches _____

____ numbness or tingling anywhere (where) _____

____ loss of balance _____

____ double vision or vision problems _____

____ periods of amnesia _____

____ mood changes _____

____ coordination changes _____

____ weakness in arms or legs _____

____ fever _____

____ nausea or diarrhea _____

____ fainting or dizziness _____

____ seizures _____

____ stressful life events such as the loss of a loved one, job changes, family or job problems

_____

____ moving _____

5. Describe your diet: _____

_____

_____

_____

Describe your use of caffeine (coffee, tea, chocolate, soft drinks):

_____

_____

Describe your use of alcohol:

_____

_____

Describe your smoking habits:

_____

Other pertinent information or concerns:

_____

_____

_____

Add pages if needed so that your physician has all needed information. You may want to mail in this information prior to your appointment and also take a copy with you.

Your physician should carefully review the information given and ask you related questions. If he or she does not do that, ask them to. If they say they don't have time, you need to insist, ask for a longer appointment, or see a different doctor.

A doctor told me that some of his patients apologize when they come to see him with extensive information and related questions. He says no apology is necessary. He appreciates the information. It makes his job easier and ensures greater success in getting to the root of problems.

You may want to take a trusted supporter with you when you have your physical examination. You have the right to have the person of your choice with you when you have your examination. People reported that they felt they got better treatment when they took someone along. It helps if you have two people that hear what the physician is saying and can ask for clarification. Your supporter can take notes while you listen and ask questions.

The following laboratory tests may be included in the examination. You can get more information on them on the internet:
    1. a complete blood count with differential (CBC)
    2. SMA 26 (26 blood chemistries and electrolytes)
    3. Thyroid tests that include Total T4, the Free T4, the total T4 and the TSH sometimes known as he BT2 panel (The drug lithium, which is commonly used to treat "bipolar disorder," can weaken the thyroid and cause low thyroid that worsens mood instability.)
    3. Serum Folate level
    4. Serum Vitamin B-12 level
    5. Urinalysis
    6. Anti-candida antibody test

Ask your doctor to explain your test results and what they indicate for your overall wellness. This is an important part of assuming responsibility for your own health. The more you know, the better the decisions you can make on your own behalf.

If all the above tests are not included in your examination, ask your doctor why. Insist on those tests that you have learned through your research are important. Advocate for yourself to get what you need. Mental health difficulties are too devastating to all facets of your life to leave any stone unturned. If your doctor refuses to address particular issues to your satisfaction, you may need to insist that he or she discusses that issue with you or refer you to someone who has more expertise.

Ask your physician for copies of all your test results. You may not understand what they mean (most of us don't), but these copies should be in your possession. The records are then available for other health care providers, eliminating the need for test duplication or time delays while new testing is completed. It also provides an accurate history of changes through the years. This is an important part of assuming responsibility for your own health.

At the end of each visit ask the doctor or the doctor's assistant to give you a complete list of follow-up action including recommendations, follow-up appointments, treatments, tests, and medications.

____ I have had a complete physical examination.

____ No follow-up appointments are needed.

____ My next appointment is (time) _____ (date) _____

____ I am not clear what the results of my examination mean.

Therefore I am going to:

_____ do some follow up research How? _____ Where? _____

_____ make a follow-up appointment with my doctor to ask more questions

____ I am not satisfied with the results of my examination.

Therefore I am going to:

____ discuss it further with my doctor.

____ discuss it with another doctor. (who) _____

What we are going to discuss:

_____
_____
_____
_____

____ Ask my doctor for a referral to a specialist What kind? _____
Why? _____

Develop a file for all of your medical records to ensure that you and your supporters have access to them when they are needed.

____ I have developed a file for all my medical records.

If your doctor advises particular medications, diet, exercise programs, or other treatment, you have a responsibility to thoroughly investigate every aspect of this recommendation. Only then will you be able to determine if it is something you are willing to do, if it is something you can do, what would stand in the way of your implementation of this treatment plan, if there are possible side effects, etc. This will facilitate every aspect of your treatment and give you more information on which to base questions to your doctor. If you are not able to do this investigation yourself, ask a trusted supporter to do it for you.

Following is an extended, but not inclusive, list of physical problems that may cause depression or mood instability. This list was prepared by Tim Field, who has responded to his health circumstances by investigating every possible cause of his depression in order to determine the best treatment course.

Possible Medical Causes of Mental Health Symptoms

(Use this list to answer question 2 in the Information for the Doctor section)

Thyroid imbalance
Adrenal gland disorders:

> Addison's Disease – may cause severe depression
> Cushing's Syndrome – may cause serious, usually "agitated" depression
> Diabetes Mellitus – especially chronic, sub-clinical and untreated may cause severe depression
> Viral Infections–such as Epstein-Barr (mononucleosis), mumps, herpes simplex
> Estrogen Deficiency in women – especially at menopause
> Pre-menstrual syndrome (PMS) in women

Drug interactions or intoxication:

> Aspirin
> Birth control pills
> Ibuprofen (Advil, Motrin, etc.)
> Arthritis medications (NSAID drugs)
> Blood pressure medications
> Anticonvulsants
> Corticosteroids
> Psychotropic (psychiatric) medication
> Over-the-counter cough or cold medication
> Tagamet (cimetidine)
> Anti-Parkinson's drugs
> Barbiturates

Drug or alcohol abuse:

     Cocaine, PCP, heroin, or marijuana

     Diet Pills

     Tranquilizers

     Amphetamines

Vitamin and Mineral deficiencies:

     Vitamin B1 (Thiamine)

     Vitamin B2 (Riboflavin)

     Vitamin B3 (Niacin)

     Vitamin B6 (Pyroxidine)

     Vitamin B12 (Cyancobalamine)

     Low or high sodium

     Vitamin C (ascorbic acid)

     Iron Deficiency

     Calcium Imbalance

     Magnesium or Zinc Deficiency

     Biotin

     Pantothenic Acid

Chronic Poisoning:

     Volatile Substances (solvents, gasoline, paint)

     Insecticides

     Carbon Monoxide

     Lead, manganese or mercury poisoning

Allergies

Ataxia telangiectasia – an inherited condition

Pituitary Gland disorder (such as Simmond's Disorder)

Diseases:

     Cancer and carcinoid syndrome

     Heart Disease

     Syphilis

     Brucella

     Tuberculosis

     Lupus

     Viral Encephalitis

Central Nervous System Disorders:

     Alzheimer's Disease

Normal Pressure Hydrocephalus

     Post-Concussion Syndrome

Multiple Sclerosis
Narcolepsy
Binswanger's Disease
Parkinson's Disease
Temporal Lobe Seizures
Other Endocrine System Disorders:
Hyperparathyroidism
Hypoparathyroidism
Pheochromocytoma
Ovarian Failure
Testicular Failure
Panhypopituitarism

The Health Care Team

As part of the complete medical evaluation, you and your physician may determine that other health care providers would be helpful in assisting with making decisions about your treatment, and for ongoing follow-up. People who get well and stay well have a carefully chosen team of health care providers to meet their individual needs. These are providers who are well-trained and have experience in addressing specific health care needs (for example, a psychiatrist, an endocrinologist, an allergist, a gynecologist, a urologist, a naturopath, a chiropractor, a nutritionist). Your health care providers need to be willing to work together and consult with each other regularly to ensure a well-coordinated approach to your health care. Your own personal preferences and needs must be considered in determining who is on your health care team.

Many people have competent, qualified health care providers, who are considered "alternative" practitioners, as an integral part of their health care team. Western and Eastern health care traditions are working more and more cooperatively, and those of us who rely on them for all, or part, of our care are reaping the benefits.

Many people report that they are tired of health care providers who give them dire projections about mental health difficulties and "diagnoses" and offer no hope. They say it aggravates rather than helping them to feel better and work on their wellness. Some people say they leave the doctor's office feeling worse than when they went in. Health care providers need to be reminded that people who experience mental health challenges can and do get well. People want, need, and deserve to feel understood, respected, supported and validated by their health care providers.

A woman who has had mental health challenges for 15 years, and has been stable for the last eight years says, "My health care support team consists of a psychiatrist who monitors my medication, a psychologist who counsels me, and a family physician who deals with issues of physical health care. My psychiatrist is supportive in both educational and employment areas. He listens to my concerns regarding mood changes and we mutually discuss medication changes. Since my long-term wellness, he has listened to my suggestions about and requests for medication and respects my self-reports."

One woman says she works together as equal partners with her psychiatrist. "The doctors should be willing to teach me what they have learned from working with other patients, give a variety of treatment options, and let me make the choices, insisting that I take responsibility for the quality of my life and the management of my illness. My doctor values and respects me and gives me hope."

A person who has both a physical disability and mental health challenges says her physician (she uses the same physician for both issues) tells her the truth no matter what without "beating around the bush" or trying to make it easier for her. She will not go to a doctor who doesn't tell her the truth or tries to handle her with "kid gloves." She says, "I want it on the line, straight to the point. I feel comfortable talking to my doctor no matter what I have to say."

All of your supporters should also have a copy of the following list. Include it in the Crisis Plan or Advance Directive section of your WRAP.

My health care team includes the following (make a copy of this list and post it in a convenient place):

My health care providers are:
Primary Care Physician _____ Phone number _____
E-mail _____

Other health care providers
Name _____ Area of Expertise _____
Phone Number _____ E-mail _____

Name _____ Area of Expertise _____
Phone Number _____ E-mail _____

Name _____ Area of Expertise _____
Phone Number _____ E-mail _____

Name _____   Area of Expertise _____

Phone Number _____   E-mail _____

Questions for the Doctor

Write a list of questions for the doctor before your appointment. Keep a pad of paper handy for several days prior to your doctor's appointment so you can jot down questions as you think of them.

Don't apologize for bringing information and questions to the doctor. A good doctor will appreciate your questions.

The following form contains some sample questions from others that you may want to ask your doctor. Check off those you want to ask your doctor. There is space at the end of this section for you to jot down any questions you want to ask the doctor.

Sample questions for your doctor:

___ *Should I be referred to an endocrinologist (a doctor that specializes in the treatment of disorders of the endocrine gland system)?*

___ *Since I have been taking lithium, has my kidney function been assessed at regular intervals? If this has not been done, why not? Can we schedule this test now?*

___ *What is a neurological exam? How could it be helpful in getting to the root of my issues?*

___ *Who will be available to answer questions and provide support when you are not available?*

___ *What kind of counseling program do you recommend?*

___ *Do you have suggestions about alternative, non-invasive treatments?*

___ *Would light therapy be helpful to me?*

___ *Are you willing to work with other health care providers on determining the most appropriate treatment for me? If not, why not?* _____

___ *When and how are the best ways to get in touch with you?*

___ *Are you willing to talk with and work with other family members or supporters if I give you permission to do so?*

Question Form

You can make copies of the following form for your own questions. Keep these sheets in your health care file for easy reference.

Question

_____

_____

Response

_____

Question

_____

_____

Response

_____

Question

_____

_____

Response

_____

Question

_____

_____

Response

_____

Question

_____

_____

Response

_____

Cost

Cost of medical care is an issue for many people. Discuss these concerns openly and honestly with your health care providers. They may be able to steer you to programs that assume some or all the costs of your treatment or medications. Advocate for health care that is equally accessible to people with all kinds of health issues and from all socio-economic levels.

Wellness and Recovery Strategies

Medication Issues

A woman who has dealt with chronic mental health issues for many years and has finally been well for several years says, "I have learned as much as I can about the medications I take. I am very in tune with how my body responds and this helps me in discussing my medication with my doctor. I have read everything I can find about the medications I take through books, articles from medical journals, the Physicians Desk Reference, psychiatric drug books, television programs or videos, newsletters, and from talking to my doctor. "

This book is not a resource for helping you make a decision whether or not to use medications, or which medications to use. Your health care providers and your own research are your best source of information on this topic. This chapter contains information on managing medications that may be useful to you.

You may use medications as part of your personal treatment and wellness program. Deciding to use medications that may affect your mood and your thinking is a personal decision that only you can make. Your decision should be based on the best information available from your health care providers and your own research.

Your physician, psychiatrist or other health care professional may recommend that you take particular medications, or you may already be taking them. In either case, there is information you need to consider if you decide these medications are part of your wellness plan.

Many people use medications as their primary way to deal with mental health problems. Some have used them for a long time. Now, more and more, people who use medications are using self help strategies to complement and enhance their medical treatment. Others use medications for the short term, to allow time to work on issues, set up systems, learn management techniques, and make lifestyle changes that promote and enhance wellness.

Appropriate medications must be determined on an individual basis by you with your doctor. Responses and medication side effects vary widely from person to person. A member of your support group may report they had excellent success with a particular medication while you may have found that the same medication was not helpful to you.

Some people resist taking psychiatric medications because they:

1. fear the long or short term side effects;

2. feel medications diminish their quality of life;

3. feel that the medications interfere with normal functioning like sexual feelings, memory, intellectual capacity, coordination, vision, and digestion;

4. feel that they are a failure if they have to use medications;

5. have ethical reasons for refusing medications; or,

6. experience intolerable side effects.

In some cases the physician is unable to find any medication or combination of medications that help the person to feel better.

If you are taking medications for your mental health issues, it is important that you:

1. are under the supervision of a physician who has extensive knowledge and experience in the use of these kinds of medications;

2. have the regular blood tests required for the medication you are taking (you can find out about needed testing on the internet);

3. do not change the amount of medication you are taking, or stop taking the medication, without consulting your physician (Systems for medication changes and discontinuation vary with each medication and must be monitored carefully to avoid potentially serious reactions. If you are having severe side effects and cannot reach your physician, contact another physician who your doctor has previously recommended as a back-up, for information on how best to deal with the situation.);

4. be completely honest with your physician about taking the medication. Tell them if you forgot to take the medication several times, didn't renew the prescription on time, etc., so the doctor can be clear about the medication effects.

If you take medications, you may find that taking them becomes so routine that you can't remember whether you have taken your dose. Some people use an empty egg carton with each egg container marked with the day of the week. The first day of each week, you fill the containers with the medications you need to take for each day of that week. A quick glance into the container will let you know whether or not you have taken that day's medications. Others set out their medications for the day in a series of cups, one for morning doses, one for noon doses, etc. Pharmacies have a variety of containers that can be used to help you keep track of your medications.

If you need to take your medication at a certain time each day, a watch with a timer signal or a small inexpensive timer can be a helpful reminder. When you realize you have missed several doses of medication, check with your physician to see if you should take the missed doses or a single dose.

Your pharmacist is a member of your health care team who is invested in your wellness. Deal with a pharmacy that has a good reputation, where the pharmacist knows you. <u>Purchase all your medications at the same pharmacy.</u>

Learn all you can about every medication you take. Have a thorough discussion with your physician and other health care providers about all aspects of the suggested medication. Use the internet to gather information. Explore a variety of viewpoints. Make copies of the following form and use it to record information about each suggested medication or treatment or any medication or treatment that is currently part of your wellness program. Make decisions on how to proceed based on your findings.

Medication Information from Your Physician

generic name _____

product name _____

product category _____

Suggested dosage level _____

How does this medication work? _____

_____

What do you expect it to do? _____

_____

_____

_____

How long will it take to achieve that result? _____

What are the risks associated with taking this medication? _____

_____

_____

What is the effectiveness record of this medication? _____

_____

What short term side effects are possible with this medication? ___

_____

_____

_____

What long term side effects are possible this medication?_____

_____

_____

_____

Is there any way to minimize the chances of experiencing these side effects? _____

If so, what are they? _____

_____

_____

_____

Are there any dietary or lifestyle suggestions or restrictions when using this medication? _____

If so, what are they? _____

_____

_____

_____

_____

Does this medication cause any adverse reactions when taken with certain other medications? _____

If so, what are they:_____
_____
_____
_____

Why do you recommend this particular medication? _____
_____
_____
_____

Have you had other patients that have used it? _____
If so, how have they done? _____
_____
_____
_____

How is this medication monitored? _____
_____
_____

What tests will I need prior to taking this medication? _____
_____
_____

What tests will I need while on the medication ? _____
_____

How often will I need these tests? _____-
What symptoms would indicate that the dosage should be changed or the medication stopped? __
_____
_____

Ask for additional printed information that can help you make your decision. Check out suggested medications on the internet. If you cannot do this yourself, ask a supporter to do it for you.

Give your supporters copies of all the information you have about the medications you are taking.

Take all medications exactly as prescribed. Follow the directions provided with the medication about how and when the medication needs to be taken. Carefully read the instructions that come with the medication. If you have questions about the how to take the medication, ask your doctor.

Medications may take from several days to several weeks, depending on the medication, before you will feel any effect.

Side Effects to Report to Your to your Physician Immediately

The following medication side effects can be serious or dangerous and need to be reported to your physician or a qualified medical provider immediately. Don't wait.

blurred vision
rapid or irregular heartbeat
rash or hives
sore throat or fever
nervousness, irritability, shakiness wanting to sleep all the time
restlessness, poor coordination
confusion
fainting, seizures, or hallucinations
numbness in your hands or feet
nausea and vomiting
mental confusion
slurred speech
stomach pains
lack of coordination, stumbling
swelling of the hands and/or feet
jerking of arms and legs
ringing in the ears
seizures or fainting
large increase in urination
complete stopping of urination
infection

Managing Side Effects

There may be safe, simple and effective ways that can help reduce or eliminate non-dangerous side effects of medications. Ask your health care provider how much water you should drink, what kind of diet you should be on, how much exercise you should get and how much rest you will need while on this medication. Your doctor or health care provider should also help you figure out simple, safe things you can do to relieve medication side effects.

Many medication side effects are most severe when you first start taking the medication and your body is adjusting. After a week or two, the side effects may diminish or disappear. Ask your physician if this is to be expected with the medication you are taking.

Keep your physician advised of all symptoms that appear after you start taking medication. Don't assume the symptom is a medication side effect and fail to report it. A serious condition that needs attention could be needlessly overlooked.

You may find that the side effects of your medication are intolerable. You may not be able to think clearly, may have digestive and elimination problems, gain excessive amounts of weight, have dry mouth, headache, dizziness or lose your sexual drive. You may have severe tremor. You deserve to feel well. Work with your doctor to find medications that will not cause you this distress.

Use the self-help techniques in this and other resources on mental health recovery so you will need only the minimal amounts of medication, if you need any medication at all.

Health care providers may minimize the importance of medication side effects, particularly low or lack of sex drive. This is not fair. People who take medications for psychiatric disabilities deserve the same kind of sexual experience as anyone else. Some people decide to switch medications or discontinue medications because of this side effect.

If the side effects of your medication are intolerable or interfere with parts of your life that you enjoy, ask your doctor to prescribe a different medication or a different treatment option.

Wellness and Recovery Strategies

Life Assessment

I knew there were some things in my life — some current and some from a long time ago — that were making things much worse.

You may feel that there was a precipitating event, series of events, life circumstances or ongoing misperceptions and guilt about past or childhood issues that preceded the onset of your mental health issues. A close look at these circumstances and issues provides important clues about factors that may make you feel worse or have a more difficult time, and provides valuable information on action you need to take to achieve recovery and a level of wellness that you are comfortable with.

Although you cannot keep traumatic events from happening or issues from influencing your thoughts and feelings, you can learn to respond to them, deal with them and work through them in ways that allow you to have more control over your moods and your life.

In addition, there may be various circumstances in your life that need to be addressed–in some cases major changes are necessary–to allow you to take charge of your own journey to wellness and stability. In this chapter we will assess those factors that may be affecting your mental health challenges.

As you consider your issues, you can determine if they are major influences–you think about them daily and they have had a major effect on the way you feel, on your life, thought patterns and lifestyle–or they are minor issues–you think about them occasionally and they have a minimal effect on how you feel and on and your life. Some of them may have been major issues at some time in your life, but due to the passage of time, life changes, and hard work, they are now only minor influences. When you complete this assessment, you can decide those issues that need immediate attention and action, and those that are important to work on for the long term.

When you have completed the assessment, the following chapters will help you explore ways you can use to minimize the effects of these issues on your life: Counseling, Exchange Listening, Focusing, Journaling and The Trauma Connection. If you have addictions, the Life Assessment process will help you decide how to address these issues.

You may find it useful to describe certain events or circumstances in detail. There is space allowed for you to do that. If this process is hard for you or brings up frightening images (called flashbacks), or makes you feel uncomfortable in any way, don't do it right now. You may want to do it slowly, over a long period of time, and when you are supported by a counselor or other person with whom you feel safe.

Sexual Abuse

Many of us report a history of childhood sexual abuse that we feel has either caused or worsened our mental health issues. You may have been diagnosed with Post Traumatic Stress Syndrome (see Trauma chapter). While it is known that sexual abuse has been going on for a long time, the understanding of its disastrous effect on the psyche of those who have experienced abuse has not been fully understood or validated until recently. Often those who reported such abuse were not believed. Upon reporting the abuse, they were told to "forgive and forget" or that they had just imagined it. The result has been poor self-esteem and ongoing serious mental health difficulties. Those of us who have worked at overcoming the effects of such abuse have regained our sense of security, worth, control over our lives and a strong sense of well being.

___ I have experienced sexual abuse.

___ I feel this abuse has a major effect on my life.

___ I feel this abuse has a minimal effect on my life.

___ I do not feel that this abuse has any effect on my life.

Describe the sexual abuse, if this feels like a safe thing for you to do at this time.

_____

_____

_____

_____

_____

Physical Abuse

You may have been physically abused by a relative, peer or stranger. Your perceptions of the relationship of this abuse to your mental health difficulties may have varied from being a major cause to having no effect at all. The severity of the abuse and whether it occurred only once, several times or was ongoing for years, seems to be significant.

___ I experienced physical abuse.

___ I feel this abuse has a major effect on my life.

___ I feel this abuse has a minimal effect on my life.

___ I do not feel that this abuse has any effect on my life.

Describe the physical abuse, if this feels like a safe thing for you to do at this time.

_____

_____

_____

_____

_____

Emotional Abuse

Long term emotional abuse takes a heavy toll on its victims. If you have been called names and verbally invalidated by authority figures, you may have low self-esteem and other issues that are affecting your life. It helps to be able to look, as adults, at the sources of this abuse and effectively counteract the associated negative thought patterns with a positive approach to self-esteem.

___ I experienced emotional abuse.

___ I feel this abuse has a major effect on my life.

___ I feel this abuse has a minimal effect on my life.

___ I do not feel that this abuse has any effect on my life.
Describe the emotional abuse, if this feels like a safe thing for you to do at this time.

_____

_____

_____

_____

_____

Marital Problems

A 46 year old woman whose relationship has weathered her recurring mental health challenges said she is always concerned that this time he will just say, "I've had it" and walk out for good. She feels that her unpredictability is creating a gap in the mutuality they once enjoyed.

___ I have marital problems or problems in a close relationship.

___ I feel this has a major effect on my life.

___ I feel this has a minimal effect on my life.

___ I do not feel that this has any effect on my life.

Describe your marital problems or your problems in a close relationship if this feels like a safe thing for you to do at this time.

_____

_____

_____

_____

_____

Divorce

A man in the study said that when he got married, he believed it would be for the rest of his life. When the marriage ended, he felt as if his life was over. That was the beginning of his mental health difficulties.

___ I am divorced.

___ I feel this has a major effect on my life.

___ I feel this has a minimal effect on my life.

___ I do not feel that this as any effect on my life.

Describe your situation with regard to divorce, if this feels like a safe thing for you to do at this time.

_____

_____

_____

_____

_____

Loss of Important People

A man reported that his wife of thirty years died suddenly and unexpectedly. That event precipitated his first serious mental health difficulties, although he had always dealt with less intrusive issues. Now he has to be vigilant in order to maintain his stability.

___ I have lost important people in my life.

___ I feel this has a major effect on my life.

___ I feel this has a minimal effect on my life.

___ I do not feel that this has any effect on my life.

Describe the loss of important people, if this feels like a safe thing for you to do at this time.

_____

_____

_____

_____

_____

Spouse Abuse

If you are being abused by a spouse or other family member, it is difficult to make any progress toward wellness. When the abuse ends, either because you leave the abusive situation or the abuser is no longer being abusive, it is much easier to work on your recovery and wellness.

___ I am being abused by my spouse or a family member.

___ I have been abused by a spouse or family member.

___ I feel this has a major effect on my life.

___ I feel this has a minimal effect on my life.

___ I do not feel that this has any effect on my life.

Describe the abuse by spouse or family member, if this feels like a safe thing for you to do at this time.

_____

_____

_____

_____

_____

Neglect

Ongoing childhood neglect is devastating. Research shows that children who have a history of repeated neglect have a much harder time resolving these issues than children who have experienced occasional abuse. If your parents were absent, or you did not have your basic needs for affection, protection, food, clothing, and warmth met consistently, you may want to work on relieving the effects that this has had on your wellness and your life.

One woman whose mother was hospitalized for long periods of time during her childhood, with no mother substitute, said she did not become aware of the connection between the neglect and her depression until the issue came up in counseling.

___ I experienced childhood neglect.

___ I feel this has a major effect on my life.

___ I feel this has a minimal effect on my life.

___ I do not feel this has any effect on my life.

Describe the neglect if this feels like a safe thing for you to do at this time.

_____

_____

_____

_____

_____

Crime Victim

The traumatic effect of crime on its victims cannot be understated. A world once considered comfortable and safe suddenly becomes a terrifying, hostile place. Those of us who have been the victim of criminal activity (i.e. robbery, muggings, rape, assault, attempted murder, etc.) noticed that the incident or incidents was the beginning of recurring mental health difficulties or worsened an already existing condition.

___ I am a crime victim.

___ I feel this has a major effect on my life.

___ I feel this has a minimal effect on my life.

___ I do not feel this has any effect on my life.

Describe the crime, if this feels like a safe thing for you to do at this time.

_____

_____

_____

_____

_____

Witness to Violence or Crime

Those of us who have witnessed violence, particularly violence against a loved one, such as a child witnessing the beating of a parent, often suffer intense, long lasting effects.

___ I witnessed violence or criminal activity.

___ I feel this has a major effect on my life.

___ I feel this has a minimal effect on my life.

___ I do not feel that this has any effect on my life.

Describe the violence or crime you witnessed if this feels like a safe thing for you to do at this time.

_____

_____

_____

_____

_____

Natural Disasters

Hurricanes, floods, earthquakes, fires, mud slides and other disasters that disrupt daily life, take away social supports and increase feelings of insecurity, take an additional toll on those of us who already have to work hard to stay well or who have experienced mental health difficulties.

___ I am a survivor of a natural disaster.

___ I feel this has a major effect on my life.

___ I feel this has a minimal effect on my life.

___ I do not feel that this has any effect on my life.

Describe your situation with regard to natural disasters, if this feels like a safe thing for you to do at this time.

_____

_____

_____

_____

_____

War

The Viet Nam War brought society to a new level of awareness of the damaging effect of wartime activity on the psyches of involved individuals. A person, who had been involved in war related actions for four years, felt that the resulting after-effects, including nightmares and flashbacks, increased his difficulty in dealing with mental health challenges that he had experienced since high school.

___ I experienced war-related action.

___ I feel this has a major effect on my life.

___ I feel this has a minimal effect on my life.

___ I do not feel that this has any effect on my life.

Describe the war-related activities you were involved in, if this feels like a safe thing for you to do at this time.

_____

_____

_____

_____

_____

Poverty

At any given time many people in the world are living in poverty without adequate resources for housing, food, clothing, health care and other necessities. If you deal with such issues on an ongoing basis, you may not have any resources left over to deal with the mental health challenges that may be a determining factor in your ongoing impoverishment–a vicious circle effect.

___ I currently live in poverty.

___ I have experienced poverty in the past.

___ I feel this has a major effect on my life.

___ I feel this has a minimal effect on my life and depressive or manic depressive episodes.

___ I do not feel that this has any effect on my life.

Describe your situation with regard to poverty if this feels like a safe thing for you to do at this time.

_____

_____

_____

_____

_____

Stigma

Terry McDonough, in "Alienation," an article in the *Western New York Mental Health World*, says, "Part of being mentally ill is worse than the disease itself: the way people respond to you. People have a tendency to walk on egg shells around you...Many people leave us out of the picture... People who don't know I'm mentally ill treat me 'normally.' If I choose to confide my condition, I'm suddenly excluded from activities in which I once participated. I'm alienated." This stigma, whether it is a response to mental health issues or to something else about you which others see as "not OK," contributes to depression and mood instability.

___ I currently experience stigma due to (mental health issues, sexual identity issues, weight, race, religion, etc.) _____.

___ I experience stigma because of (mental health issues, sexual preference, weight, race, religion, etc.) _____in the past.

___ I feel this has a major effect on my life.

___ I feel this has a minimal effect on my life.

___ I do not feel that this has any effect on my life.

Describe your situation with regard to stigma, if this feels like a safe thing for you to do at this time.

_____
_____
_____
_____
_____

Inability to Follow Your Own Path

A man reported that as far back as he could remember, people in his family assumed he would be a medical doctor. As he grew up he accepted the idea. When he began medical school he had his first mental health difficulties. These difficulties became less frequent when he realized his talents and interests were in teaching, and pursued that career.

___ I have been unable to follow my own path and to pursue the career goals or vocation of my choice, because _____

_____

_____ I feel this has a major effect on my life.

_____ I feel this has a minimal effect on my life.

_____ I do not feel that this has any effect on my life.

Describe your situation regarding your inability to follow the path of your choice, if this feels like a safe thing for you to do at this time.

_____

_____

_____

_____

_____

Work Stress

A woman reported that she was employed for many years by a major corporation. She was comfortable in her work and enjoyed it very much. She had always assumed that she would work there until she retired. Several years ago, the demand for the product produced by her company decreased sharply, in response to a sluggish economy. Many employees were laid off. She was not sure when it would be her turn. In addition, she was expected to work overtime and take on additional responsibilities to make up for employees who had lost positions. She had been dealing with mental health issues for a long time. With this increased pressure and lack of security, these difficulties worsened.

_____ I am currently under excessive work-related stress.

_____ I feel this has a major effect on my life.

_____ I feel this has a minimal effect on my life.

_____ I do not feel that this has any effect on my life.

Describe your situation with regard to work related stress, if this feels like a safe thing for you to do at this time.

_____

_____

_____

_____

_____

Do you feel there is any way you could reduce the work-related stress at this time? _____
If so, how?_____

_____

_____

If not, why not? _____

_____

_____

Loneliness

If you have experienced ongoing mental health issues, you may have few close friends and have lost connections with family members. You may feel lonely much of the time.

___ I am lonely.

___ I feel this has a major effect on my life.

___ I feel this has a minimal effect on my life.

___ I do not feel that this has any effect on my life.

Describe your situation with regard to loneliness, if this feels like the right thing for you to do at this time.

_____

_____

_____

_____

_____

Poor Social Skills

A woman in her forties, who had mental health difficulties for many years said that she realized, after long term work with an empathetic counselor, that her strong tendency to be a "chatterbox" overwhelmed others. They had been reluctant to point this out to her because of her mental health issues, withdrawing from her instead.

____ I feel that I have poor social skills.

____ I feel this has a major effect on my life.

____ I feel this has a minor effect on my life.

____ I do not feel that this has any effect on my life.

Describe your problems with social skills, if this feels like a safe thing for you to do at this time.

_____

_____

_____

_____

_____

Physical Challenges or Disabilities

A 41 year-old woman who has been mental having health issues since the age of 14, feels that her physical difficulties, including a shunt for hydrocephalus caused by a pre-birth injury, head injuries caused by a severe beating, poor vision, and, constant leg and back pain, have contributed to mental health problems.

____ I have physical health challenges.

____ I feel this has a major effect on my life.

____ I feel this has a minor effect.

____ I do not feel that this has had any effect on my life.

Describe your physical challenges, if this feels like a safe thing for you to do at this time.

_____
_____
_____
_____
_____

Illness

If you deal with chronic medical illnesses, you may find that these conditions aggravate your mental health issues. Illnesses such as diabetes, multiple sclerosis, tuberculosis, or Parkinson's disease make it difficult to work on wellness and recovery.

___ I have a (chronic or acute) _____ illness.

___ I feel this has a major effect on my life.

___ I feel this has a minimal effect on my life.

___ I do not feel this has any effect on my life.

Describe your chronic or acute illness, if this feels like the right thing for you to do at this time.

_____
_____
_____
_____
_____

Other Life Circumstances That are Affecting Your Mental Health Issues

Issue _____

_____

___ I feel this has a major effect on my life.

___ I feel this has a minimal effect on my life.

___ I do not feel that this has any effect on my life.

Describe the issue, if this feels like the right thing for you to do at this time.

_____

_____

_____

_____

_____

Immediate Action Needed

Those life situations that are a serious threat to your safety, such as being abused, demand immediate attention and action. Make a list of those situations that need immediate attention and action. Describe what you are going to do to relieve the situation and protect yourself.

Situation _____

Action you are going to take _____

_____

When and how you are going to take this action _____

_____

Who is going to support you as you take this action?_____

_____

_____

_____

Situation _____

Action you are going to take _____

_____

When and how you are going to take this action _____

_____

Who is going to support you as you take this action?_____

_____

_____

_____

Long Term Intensive Work

Review the list of issues again. What is affecting your mental health that needs long term intensive work? What problems do you know you can't resolve overnight, but you know must be addressed over the long run, for you to work on your recovery and wellness?

_____

_____

_____

_____

_____

Which issues do you feel are not appropriate to address at this time but will need attention in the future?

_____

_____

_____

_____

_____

In the next chapters we will discuss using counseling, exchange listening, focusing, journaling, and recovering from trauma as strategies you can use to relieve the effects of these issues in your life. You can also use the Wellness Recovery Action Plan described in Chapters 4-9 of this book to resolve issues and work toward recovery and wellness.

In addition there are many excellent self-help books that can help you with these issues You can easily locate them on the internet and in your local library and bookstore.

Addictions

Substance Abuse

It is difficult to overcome mental health problems if you are addicted to alcohol or drugs. You may feel like you actually got involved with the use of alcohol or drugs in your quest to find relief from ongoing depression or manic depression.

___ I have abused substances (alcohol or drugs) in the past.

___ I currently abuse substances (alcohol or drugs).

___ I feel substance abuse has a major effect on my life.

___ I feel substance abuse has a minimal effect on my life.

___ I do not feel that substance abuse has any effect on my life.

Describe your situation with regard to substance abuse, if this feels like the right thing for you to do at this time.

_____

_____

_____

_____

_____

____ I am going to work on giving up my addiction to alcohol/drugs.

Detoxification from alcohol or drug addictions can cause severe medical symptoms. If you possibly can, go through this process at a detoxification center. It is dangerous to detoxifiy without medical and other supports. Also, the process can be so painful that you will resort to using the addictive substance to help relieve the pain. A complete physical examination, before treatment begins, will address any medical conditions that might affect your progress.

After you have gone through the detoxification process, a specialized rehabilitation program can help prevent relapse. You can get information on detoxification and rehabilitation programs from your doctor, other health care providers, hospitals, mental health and social service agencies, drug /alcohol rehabilitation agencies, members of twelve-step programs, the library and the phone book.

____ I am going to enter a detoxification program to deal with my addiction.

___ I am going to get information on how to do this from (see list above) _____.

List as many people as you can that you can safely turn to for guidance, assistance and support in this process.

_____

_____

_____

_____

_____

_____

If you don't feel anyone will support you in this way, don't let that stop you. As you begin the treatment process, you will meet new supporters.

If addictions to alcohol or drugs are long term issues, you may need several courses of treatment. Don't get discouraged. Your life is worth it.

Other Addictions

There are many addictions that impede the progress of people who are seeking to recover from mental health challenges. For instance, a woman in the study said she had a food addiction that has caused her obesity–she was 100 pounds overweight. This addiction lowered her self-esteem and made her sluggish and depressed. Coming to terms with addictions, and letting go of them, gives a huge boost to wellness efforts.

In order to address addictions, most of us need professional help and ongoing support.

___ I am addicted to (food, nicotine, sex, caffeine, chocolate, sugar, etc.)_____

___ I have been addicted to (food, nicotine, sex, caffeine, chocolate, sugar, etc.) in the past.

___ I feel this has a major effect on my life.

___ I feel this has a minimal effect on my life.

___ I do not feel that this has any effect on my life.

Describe your addictions, if this feels like the right thing for you to do at this time.

_____
_____
_____
_____
_____

____ I going to work on giving up my addiction to (name) _____

List as many people as you can that you can safely turn to for guidance, assistance and support in this process.

_____

_____

_____

_____

_____

There are many organizations that specialize in supporting you as you work to give up your addictions. You can easily locate them on the internet. You can learn of organizations and resources in your area through:

- your doctor
- hospitals
- drug /alcohol rehabilitation agencies
- library
- newspaper
- other health care providers
- mental health and social service agencies
- members of twelve-step programs
- phone book

Wellness and Recovery Strategies

Trauma Issues

I always felt something was wrong with me, like I was somehow "tainted."
I didn't know where these feelings came from, and I couldn't make them go away.

Many of the people I studied who have gotten well and stayed well, reported that they had experienced a trauma, or a series of traumas, such as physical, sexual or emotional abuse, neglect, being a crime victim, surviving a natural disaster, or seeing a violent act against a loved one. You may feel that trauma has caused or worsened your mental health difficulties. You may have been diagnosed with Post Traumatic Stress Disorder (PTSD). You may have worked through a program designed to reduce signs of Post Traumatic Stress Disorder that helped you to feel better.

Post Traumatic Stress Disorder was only recognized as a disorder in 1980, in response to symptoms exhibited by veterans of the Vietnam War. It soon became apparent that those who experienced other traumas, not necessarily related to war experiences, had similar symptoms. Because it was recognized so recently, many people who have PTSD go unrecognized, and do not receive needed help and support.

Some people, who cannot remember a specific traumatic event or series of traumatic events, have signs of Post Traumatic Stress Disorder. In these instances, the trauma may have occurred before the development of their memory, they may have repressed the memory, or they may not have recognized the experience as abuse, such as in the case of long term neglect or emotional abuse. Whether one remembers the trauma or not, addressing symptoms through using the safe methods described in this chapter and *Healing the Trauma of Abuse: A Workbook for Women* (Copeland, Harris. 1999. Oakland, CA: New Harbinger Publications.).

The effects of abuse and trauma have traditionally been ignored by some health care workers, family members, and supporters. Like many others, you may prefer to avoid or deny, rather than deal with horrible incidents. Many abuse survivors have discounted the effects of trauma on their lives because when they reported the trauma, they were not believed, or the effects of the trauma were not validated. You may have been told, "it was your fault," to "forgive and forget," or to just "get on with your life." Because of the presenting symptoms, you may have been diagnosed with a major mental illness and have had repeated psychiatric hospitalizations.

Instead of putting the blame where it belongs – on the perpetrator, or in the case of a natural disaster – on "an act of God," many people tend to take full responsibility for what happened to them, assuming that they are at fault. They attribute it to some basic character flaw, erroneously concluding that somehow, their actions caused terrible things to happen to them and they deserve what they get.

You may perpetuate yourself in the victim role by using adaptation devices such as denial, dissociation, and not allowing yourself to feel. The abuse or trauma becomes the basis for your self-perception and your relationship to others, and the world.

You might become aware that a traumatic event or series of traumatic events, or that past or current chronic physical, sexual or emotional abuse, or neglect, is causing or worsening your mental health difficulties in several ways.

1. You may have always been aware that remembered or current abuse was causing your mental health problems.

2. You went to a mental health center, counselor, or emergency room for help treatment and it was suggested that your difficulties may be the result of abuse.

3. You begin to have memories or flashbacks of trauma or abusive incidents.

If shortly after the abuse or trauma occurred, remedial action such as validation, understanding, respect, and support begins, the negative effects of the experience may diminish. This often happens in today's society. If a trauma occurs in a school, special counselors are brought in to deal with student reactions. People who are crime victims may receive intensive counseling and support. In cases where this support is not forthcoming, in cases of abuse where others do not know the abuse is occurring, or where the event or series of events happened in the past, the mental health difficulties may persist and become overwhelming.

These problems may be more intense and acute if the onset of abuse occurred at an early age, before you could accurately assess what was happening, and you were not old enough to be responsible for your own safety, if a supposed trusted adult was the perpetrator, if it occurred over a long period of time, if there was physical violence and if coercion or deception were involved. The longer abuse goes untreated, the greater the repression, and the more ingrained the symptoms.

Recovering from abuse and trauma is a process of reducing the effects of the trauma in our lives and integrating such events in positive ways into our life story. It takes time and persistence.

Don't expect miracles overnight. Sometimes you will make a lot of progress. At other times you will need to take a break from this work and focus on other parts of your life. Everyone's path to healing and recovery is different.

SIGNS OF POST TRAUMATIC STRESS DISORDER

Do you experience many of the following signs of Post Traumatic Stress Disorder?

____ mood instability

____ depression

____ nightmares

____ insomnia or sleep disturbances

____ flashbacks (recurring intrusive thoughts, feelings and images of trauma)

____ unexplainable outbursts of temper

____ feeling always on the alert (hyperarousal)

____ dissociation (feeling that you are not in your body, a feeling of disconnection from yourself and life experiences)

____ feeling like you are unsafe in your body

____ anxiety and panic attacks

____ feeling out of control

____ feeling like your emotions and thought processes are out of control

____ poor self-esteem

____ lack of self confidence

____ inability to experience pleasure

____ unexplainable grief reactions

____ hopelessness

____ poor concentration

____ difficulty making decisions

____ alcohol and substance abuse

____ food or other addictions

____ self-destructive acts

____ suicidal thoughts

____ attempted suicides

____ episodes of heightened anxiety

____ sexual problems

____ re-victimization (abuse continues to occur)

____ a vague feeling that something unidentifiable is wrong with you

____ desire to hurt yourself or self-mutilation

____ social isolation

_____ inability to trust appropriate people

_____ lack of confidence in the future

_____ feeling powerless to create change in your life

_____ uncontrolled fear

_____ chronic muscle tension

_____ feeling that nothing makes sense

List other signs that you feel may indicate that your mental health difficulties are related to experiences of abuse or trauma.

_____

_____

_____

_____

_____

WHAT HAPPENS

When trauma occurs you lose:

- your sense of connection to others (you feel alone and isolated, unable to feel close to anyone).

- your sense of self (because of what happened or the response of others to what happened, you feel invalidated as a human being).

- your sense of power, control over your life and safety (you feel like everything that happens is out of your control).

THE RECOVERY PROCESS

Recovery includes re-establishing your connection with other people, validation of your life experience and regaining power and control over your life, and learning how to keep yourself safe.

The following steps to recovery can be worked on simultaneously or separately. You are in charge of your recovery process. It needs to feel right to you.

Establish Safety

If you have been abused or traumatized, you may tend to recreate circumstances which allow for continuation of abuse or trauma related events. You may continue to live in chaotic, violent, and volatile relationships, with a person, or persons, who continue to physically or emotionally abuse you, and do not support and protect you. You might find yourself spending time or living in places that are not safe. You may spend time in bars and sections of town where there is a lot of action but no protection. Breaking the cycle by providing yourself with safe places, and connecting with people who respect and care for you, helps to change this destructive pattern.

For several years I lived with a husband who threatened me, threatened my family, was emotionally abusive, and occasionally physically attacked me. My low self-esteem connected with childhood issues led me to believe I deserved this treatment. Through a good counseling program, and self-help trauma-related recovery work, I realized that I needed to leave that situation and find space for myself with safe people.

_____ I spend time with people who treat me well and respect me.

_____ The people I spend time with are sometimes hostile and abusive and do not contribute to my sense of safety and well being.

_____ I need to spend time with people who are respectful, caring, and supportive.

Therefore, I will spend time with:

_____

_____

_____

_____

_____

I will avoid:

_____

_____

_____

_____

_____

The actual space where you live may not be safe. It may be in a section of town where there is a high crime rate. The space may not be secure. It may not have good locks, strong doors, and other barriers, allowing easy access to anyone who wants to enter. The space may be too isolated for easy access to help and protective services.

I lived for a time in a quaint, rustic log house in the country. It seemed idyllic. However, its isolation from other people and protective services allowed easy access to anyone who may have wanted to hurt me. The locks were flimsy. There were no alternative routes to use in leaving the house. I could never relax there, especially at night, when the surrounding forest seemed dark and foreboding.

I now live in a house with good locks and strong doors, not easily accessible by people who do not live here. I have family members who would assist me in difficult circumstances. I have a wonderful dog that lets me know when anyone is around.

_____ I live in a safe space.

I feel safe in this space because (For example, I have a dog, the locks are secure, it is close to other people who would protect me):

_____

_____

_____

_____ I do not live in a safe place.
_____ I am too vulnerable in my present living space.
_____ It is not in a safe section of town.
_____ It cannot be adequately locked to prevent access by others.
_____ It is not close to others who would protect me, or protective services.

Other reasons you do not feel safe in this space:

_____

_____

_____

_____

_____ I need to find space to live where I am safe. This means (describe action you are going to take to find yourself a safe space to live):

_____

_____

_____

_____

_____

_____

REBUILDING SUPPORT AND TRUST

Sometimes, when you have been traumatized or abused, you lose your trust of others and isolate yourself. You may have plenty of acquaintances, but cannot feel close to anyone. Reconnecting with people who validate your experience, who affirm you, who are supportive and worthy of your trust, is an essential step in the healing process. Support groups, health care providers, including a counselor, and trusted family and friends who respect your healing process, will help you reconnect with positive people.

Health care providers and supporters that assist you as you work through the healing process:
- validate your experience, listen to what you are reporting, and believe you.
- give appropriate advice, encouragement, care and support that is always under your control.
- understand clearly that the control of the process must remain with you.
- assist you in reclaiming your power.
- help you redefine yourself as a separate person in charge of yourself and your life.
- reduce your sense of loneliness and isolation.
- recognize your experiences, strengths and abilities.
- direct you to resources.

In my own case, I didn't share information about my abuse history because when I was a child, I told adults (who were supposed to be protecting me), about the abuse. I was told that *it must have been my fault* and *to forgive and forget*. I felt that there must be something wrong with me, rather than the truth, that something was very wrong with the abusers. I withdrew and avoided contact with others. Even as an adult I felt distanced from others, that no one really liked me, and that I was not a lovable person.

I have learned, as many others have, to reconnect with other people, through years of counseling, exchange listening , support groups, getting involved in activities with people I enjoy, and working on changing negative beliefs about myself to positive ones.

Counseling

While not necessary to recovery, many people who are healing from the effects of trauma choose to work with a trusted counselor who will support and guide them through the process. The counselor assists the recovery process by becoming an ally, sharing useful knowledge, resources, techniques, possible solutions, and experiences.

The relationship with the counselor must be one of equality. You are in charge of your healing process. The counselor assists you in that process. The old model where the counselor played the role of benevolent parent does not work in dealing with trauma issues. It is a constant reminder of trauma where power is taken over by another person. The counselor presents choices, but does not make decisions. Directed intervention is only valid if you are a clear and indisputable danger to yourself or others; but even then, you need to be given as much choice as possible.

There are many counselors trained to work with people who are recovering from the effects of trauma. Get referrals from your physician, mental health center, crisis center, or help line. The availability of counseling may be limited by financial considerations. See the chapter entitled "Counseling" for more information on finding a counselor.

_____ I am already working on these issues in counseling.

_____ I am going to establish an ongoing relationship with a counselor.

_____ I am going to see (name of counselor) _____.

_____ I don't know who I am going to see. I am going to find someone by _____
_____

_____ I am not going to use counseling as a resource. Why not?
_____
_____

Support Groups

In many areas, support groups are available, often free of charge, for people who have been or are being abused or traumatized. They give you an opportunity to share what has happened to you, for acceptance and validation, to help you to understand what "really" happened to you, to promote feelings of safety, and provide an opportunity for developing close, positive relationships. You will also find out that you are not alone, that others feel the way you do, and have had similar experiences. Through support groups, you will see that others, with symptoms like you have, get better.

While the size of groups vary, five to seven people seems to work best. Most meet weekly, but may choose to meet more often when the group is first starting. The criteria for being a member of the group is that you come from a background which includes abuse or trauma, and that you agree to confidentiality, and other rules that members of the group agree on. In addition to sharing, validation, and connection, group members may work together to develop individual safety plans, and create safety strategies.

Discussion includes such issues as flashbacks (what they are and where they come from), the difference between flashbacks and hallucinations, delusions, being considered "crazy," and issues around cutting. Group members may review safety plans, learn relaxation and stress reduction exercises, write letters to perpetrators, and discuss activities that will help them to understand their own power.

Ask your counselor, call the crisis center, or the help line in your area, or check the local newspaper for more information about support groups in your area. The group should be a comfortable, safe place, where you can share your experience, and be validated and affirmed. If you do not feel comfortable in a group after several sessions, locate another group which feels comfortable to you.

_____ I am already in a support group.

_____ I am going to join a support group. I am going to find a support group by

_____

_____ I am not going to go to a support group. Why not?

_____
_____
_____

See Chapter 3, Support.

Exchange Listening

Exchange Listening lets you share and integrate memories, thoughts, and feelings safely, supported by a person you trust. Many people prefer Exchange Listening for this work because they feel in charge, it is free, and they are giving something back to the other person. (It is discussed in the chapter "Exchange Listening".)

_____ I Exchange Listen.

_____ I am going to try Exchange Listening.

I am going to Exchange Listen with:

_____

_____

_____

_____

How often? ____ daily ____ weekly ____ twice a week ____ other-specify _____

____ I am not going to use Exchange Listening because:

_____

_____

_____

Activities

A good way to reconnect with people is to join others in activities of mutual interest. I like to hike and cross country ski. I often ask friends to join me on these excursions. When people are engaged in an enjoyable activity together, it helps them to feel safe and comfortable.

I am going to ask the following people to join me in activities:

_____

_____

_____

_____

_____

Activities I can share with friends:

_____

_____

_____

_____

_____

Remembering and Sharing

Sharing abuse memories can take away their power and help us to re-evaluate experiences and feel better. Sharing memories needs to be done in a safe place where validation is assured. You need to be able to say whatever you think and feel, even if you don't know whether or not it is real. You need to be able to repeat the same thing over and over, to say it any way you want, and to express any emotion you feel in this process. No one else should put any pressure on this process. You share when you are ready, and only what you want to share.

Keep the process of uncovering and sorting out memories and experiences contained. Don't let them take control and overwhelm your life. For instance, set aside a block of time with a counselor or trusted peer to work on these issues. Complete the session with an activity that brings you back to the present, like talking about what you are planning to wear to work the next day, what you are planning to have for supper, your impression of a current event or an event you are looking forward too. This trauma is part of the past. Don't allow it to overtake and continue to rob you of your life. Set parameters around the time you use to work on these issues. Then spend the rest of your time focused on the present, taking care of your responsibilities and doing things you enjoy.

Thoughts, feelings, and flashbacks sometimes intrude and become obsessive, triggered by some factor in the environment you may, or may not, be aware of. When thoughts, feelings, or flashbacks become overwhelming, it helps to talk to a supportive person about them, write them down, or express them through an artistic medium such as drawing with paints, markers, or working with clay. Whatever you choose, do it until you feel like you don't need to do it anymore and you feel better. Write until it is all out of you for the time being. Paint until you don't feel like painting any more. Talk until there is nothing more to say. Don't worry about style, technique, etc. Whatever comes out is acceptable. You are in charge of this process. It is up to you to decide what you are going to do and how you are going to do it.

Take good care of yourself in every way while you are doing this work, as you should at all times. Eat right. Exercise. Keep your living space attractive. Do activities you enjoy. Spend time with people you really like. Honor yourself and your experience.

At some point, you may think you have dealt with every trauma-related issue that ever affected you. Then you read an article in the paper, hear a name, feel a breeze blow across your face in a particular way, and all the feelings are back. This happens. You cannot predict when it is going to happen. Be gentle with yourself. Use techniques you have used throughout the healing process to help you feel better.

Changing negative beliefs about yourself to positive ones

Trauma and abuse experiences cause those of us who have experienced abuse and trauma to develop negative, inaccurate and inappropriate beliefs about ourselves that are not true, and hamper the recovery process. You need to build a new view of yourself and of the world. A process of identifying negative beliefs, changing them to positive ones, sometimes called cognitive therapy, facilitates the recovery process. You will find yourself building a whole new self-image based on reality, rather than an image imposed upon you by a person, persons or some event.

The following negative beliefs are typical of those held by people who have been traumatized. They can be changed by developing a positive rebuttal statements and repeating these statements over and over to yourself, until you know and believe they are true.

Nobody ever liked me.
List people who have liked you:

_____

_____

_____

_____

_____

Nobody likes me.
Many people like me.

List people who like you.

_____

_____

_____

_____

_____

I have never been safe.
I have been safe.

List times when you have been safe:

_____

_____

_____

_____

_____

There have never been any positive people in my life.
List the positive people in your life.

_____

_____

_____

_____

_____

I am a bad person.
Change to: The people and things that happened to me were bad. I am not bad.

The bad things that happened to me were my fault.
Change to: The bad things that happened to me were not my fault.

I can't take care of myself.
Change to: I am a competent capable adult now. I can take care of myself. No one can do bad things to me. I keep myself safe. I stay away from people who do bad things. I am powerful. I am in control of myself and my life.

I deserve to be treated badly.
Change to: I deserve to be treated with dignity and respect at all times.

I do not deserve to be alive.
Change to: I have a right to be alive.

I want to die
Change to: I want to live. I deserve to live.

My body is dirty.
Change to: My body is clean and wonderful.

Sex is bad.
Change to: Sex is a beautiful thing when shared by people who love and respect each other.

I don't trust myself, my thoughts or my feelings.
Change to: I trust myself, my thoughts and my feelings.

I am not in charge of my life.
Change to: I am in charge of my life.

I can't do anything good for myself.
Change to: I can take positive action on my own behalf.

I can't do anything right.
Change to: I do many things well. They include:

_____

_____

_____

_____

_____

I have never accomplished anything.
Change to: I have accomplished many things in my life. They include:

_____

_____

_____

_____

_____

I never feel close to anyone.
Change to: I feel close to many people. They include:

_____

_____

_____

_____

_____

Write a personal positive affirmation of yourself that you can repeat over and over. For instance, one that I have used as part of my recovery is:

I am an amazing person for having survived. I am responsible for getting myself to this good place where I am in charge of my life and my recovery. I am an amazing person. I have created a safe place for myself in the world.

Your personal affirmation:

_____

_____

_____

_____

_____

Change the way you feel about yourself by nurturing yourself. Those of us who have been traumatized or victimized often have the misperception that we do not have any value and do not deserve anything good in our lives. Consequently, we do not treat ourselves well. To contradict this negative thinking, we need to treat ourselves very well. Pretend you are your own best friend. Then do for yourself as you would do for this friend.

Make your living space very comfortable and pleasant for yourself. This may involve some redecorating. If cost is a problem, inexpensive and attractive coverlets, curtains, rugs, and accessories can often be purchased at rummage or yard sales or thrift stores. Think of the kind of space that would nourish you and create it for yourself. If you live with others, this may need to be just your room or a part of a room.

<u>Avoid the company of people who do not treat you well</u>.

Eat well. Prepare food for yourself that you enjoy and then serve it in style. Odd pieces of very lovely china can be purchased at yard sales and flea markets.

Treat yourself regularly to a soothing, warm bath instead of a hurried shower.

Spend some time each day doing something you really enjoy like painting, sewing, going to a movie, talking with a friend, playing basketball.

Wear clothes that you enjoy and that look nice on you.

I am going to do the following things to nurture myself:

_____

_____

_____

_____

_____

Self-empowerment

Empowering yourself to take positive action on your own behalf will be essential to your recovery program.

You must be in total control of every aspect of your own recovery. Others are involved in the process to validate you and your experience, and to offer advice, support, assistance, affection and care. Only you can heal yourself. This is essential to regaining power over your life. If any person, whether they are a health care provider or a member of your support team, insists that you take action under their direction, they are not supportive and cannot be included in your recovery process. The recovery process is very personal and only you can be in charge.

One woman said that as an abuse victim, she regained her power by insisting on her rights whenever appropriate, becoming an advocate for others who have been abused, and by working on a committee that is developing a safe place for abuse victims.

Ways that you can help yourself feel empowered (check the ones you are going to pursue):

_____ Take a self defense course.

_____ Volunteer for the local crisis, help or hotline.

_____ Advocate for abuse victims and survivors.

_____ Volunteer at a crisis center.

_____ Study self help resources on assertiveness, advocacy and self-empowerment.

_____ Take an assertiveness training course.

Other ways you can empower yourself:

_____

_____

_____

_____

_____

Important Points about your Recovery Process

Your recovery program needs to be:

- flexible – based on your own needs and feelings. (No one can define your recovery process for you. It is uniquely yours and needs to proceed as you see fit. There my be times when you work on recovery intensely and other times when you choose not to deal with trauma related issues.)

- directed by you. (You need to ask for what you need and want for yourself, persisting until you get it.)

- focused on your strengths.

- sensitive to issues related to your age, culture, religion, race, gender, and sexual identity.

When flashbacks overtake you, be with them, honor them for the role the experiences have played in making you the wonderful person that you are, and then let them go. Try not to let flashbacks and feelings overwhelm you. Understand that, while this happened to you, it is not happening now. Concentrate on the present time as much as possible.

Replace these feelings by doing things you enjoy.

Things I will do to take my attention away from flashbacks and the bad things that happened to me:

_____

_____

_____

_____

Those of us who have experienced trauma or abuse, often have the uncomfortable and unsettling feeling of being in a constant state of hyperarousal. Use relaxation and stress reduction techniques to reduce these feelings.

You may have used, or are using, medication to reduce feelings that are overwhelming and to allow them to begin their recovery process. If you are considering using medications, review the chapter on "Medication Issues."

Wellness and Recovery Strategies

Counseling

This journey is difficult. My counselor has been there with me through all the hard times. Her support has been consistent and unwavering.

Many people who have gotten well and stayed well have used counseling as part of their overall treatment strategy. Before the discovery of today's medical treatments, counseling, or psychotherapy, was the one of the few options for people with mental health challenges. Today we have many more choices, and counseling is often recommended as one of several strategies used concurrently with others to facilitate recovery and wellness.

Many people consider counseling a confiding relationship you establish with a person specially trained in this field. It gives you an opportunity to share your experiences and predicaments. It often helps you feel better, by assisting you in developing a deeper understanding of yourself, and teaching you new approaches to life situations. Counseling can include listening, encouragement, support, understanding, monitoring, feedback, advice, information and education. Many people benefit from this kind of support. One woman in counseling said, " *Change doesn't just happen by the magic of the counselor or the process. A commitment to the wellness process and a willingness to work are imperative.*"

The kinds of counseling vary as much as the people involved in the counseling relationship. Most counselors use a variety of approaches, depending on what works best for the individual. If you want more information on specific kinds of counseling, you can search it on the internet or find books on the topic.

Feedback from a person who has been in a variety of counseling situations was:
My bias is that non-directive counseling is the best kind, <u>except in crisis management</u>. It allows you to discover yourself, rather than get the shorter term superficial fix of becoming what the counselor thinks you should be. People generally don't like being told what to do. That approach is not helpful to healing.

In the Life Assessment chapter, you may have noted issues in your life that need to be addressed. Counseling is one way to work on these issues, find solutions to problems and help you feel better. You may want to share your writings in that chapter with your counselor.

_____ I am going to share my writings in the "Life Assessment" chapter with my counselor.

The Counseling Experience

Consider the following descriptions of the counseling experience from various people. Note the variety and individuality.

A woman who has been successful in stabilizing her moods, after years of severe mental health difficulties, says: *"I work through situation-based tensions. It puts structure in my day and helps me to be more creative in problem solving. At a counseling session, I talk about whatever feelings arise out of situations that I have experienced. The counselor challenges my negative thoughts about myself. She lets me know when she sees changes in my behavior, and gives me positive feedback on my progress. The counseling, which I have been in for 15 years, has created a great deal of change in my life. An ideal counselor would allow you to unfold your complexities as you are ready, and encourage you to look at the good as well as the problem areas."*

A man in his mid-fifties who has had recurring mental health issues said: *"Counseling helps me to know myself better by giving me some outside feedback. I have a tendency to get into negative thinking, when I am feeling more down, and into risky behavior when I am higher, so getting feedback about these things helps me to be more grounded. We discuss any significant changes in mood, medication as prescribed by my physician, and ways I have dealt with these things. Positive thinking is reinforced."*

A man in his forties said that he has a tendency to downplay changes, especially when his mood starts going higher. *"My counselor challenges my irrational thoughts and helps me to be more grounded in reality. I may not like what he says at times but I can trust him to be honest and helpful."*

One woman said that counseling is helpful to her because it gives her a chance to share her thoughts and feelings without being judged. She says her counselor shares her excitement when she shares her hopes of changing (or helping to change) attitudes and opportunities for others with these issues.

A man in his sixties, who has experienced deep depressions for 20 years, said counseling helps him *"distinguish between the things I can have an impact on, and can change, and those I cannot."*

One man, who has had a five-year hiatus from any mental difficulties, says that he expects counseling to be able to change his thinking and get rid of the negative emotions, like anger, fear, low self-confidence and low self-esteem. It has helped him accept himself as he is, accept others as they are, practice detachment with other people, and has helped him in setting short and long term goals that are realistic.

What would you like counseling to do for you?

_____

_____

_____

_____

_____

If you tell others that you are considering counseling, they may say "Aren't you over that yet?" That kind of feedback is not helpful. It is up to you to decide what you need to do for yourself. And keep in mind, there are some things that happen to us in life that we may never get over. We just figure out how to live with them as well as we possibly can.

You may also get feedback on how long you are in counseling. Others may suggest that it is time to stop counseling. Again, these decisions are totally up to you. Unless there are insurance implications, you, and only you, decide when you are ready to stop counseling.

Choosing a Counselor

Try to choose your counselor when you are doing well, not when you are in the midst of a crisis or having early warning signs. It is helpful to have in place a counselor who knows you and your situation, knows about your mental health challenges and who can give good advice and support when you are having a difficult time. Your counselor is your steadfast ally on the road to recovery. (Mine has been just that to me. I have had the same counselor for over 20 years and I still see her on a regular basis.)

_____ I am going to establish a relationship with a counselor when I am feeling well.

Why do you feel it is important to have a counselor?

_____

_____

_____

_____

____ I am not going to establish a counseling relationship. Why not?

_____

_____

_____

_____

Choosing a counselor is a very personal matter. Regardless of the counselor's credentials, experience and reputation, the only counselor that can work effectively with you is one you respect, whose judgment you value, and with whom you have rapport. Health insurance plans, family members, friends and supporters may try to steer you in one direction or another. Choose the counselor you feel most comfortable with, who you think will be most helpful to you.

Effective counselors can have varied educational backgrounds, from associates to doctoral degrees. Counselors with more advanced degrees will have more supervised counseling experience, more information, and more experience with a variety of counseling techniques. They may have researched specific areas of interest. Some counselors have specialized training in specific subjects. However, some excellent counselors do not have impressive academic credentials or educational experience.

____ The counselors educational background is important to me.

Why? _____

_____

I prefer a counselor with the following educational background. _____

_____

The counselor's educational background is not important to me.
Why not? _____

_____

Counselors will vary in the amount of experience they have. Some will have been counselors for many years, while others, such as graduate students or interns, are just beginning their counseling career. Some will have an extensive background in working with people with mental health challenges. Others, particularly those who practice in rural communities, work with people with a variety of issues.

____ The counselor's experience is important to me. Why?

_____ The counselor's experience is not important to me. Why not?

_____

_____

As you search for the right counselor, you may hear various anecdotal and informational reports on particular counselors. Consider whether the source is reliable, and whether the issues discussed are valid to you. For instance, someone might say she wouldn't go to a particular a counselor because the counselor was too young and that their age difference would limit the effectiveness of the counseling. This is not an issue for everyone. You may have heard that a particular counselor had not been as supportive as someone thought they should be. How important are such reports to you?

_____ My counselor's reputation is important to me. Why?

_____

_____

_____ My counselor's reputation is not important to me. Why not?

_____

_____

Many women say they would prefer working with a female counselor, and many men say they would prefer working with a male. They feel that having a counselor of the same sex allows them to be more open about personal issues, and that a same-sex counselor would have a deeper level of experience of their issues.

_____ I would prefer having a counselor of the same sex. Why?

_____

_____

_____The gender of the counselor is not important to me. Why not?

_____

_____

You may prefer to work with a counselor who is willing to confer with other health care providers as needed, and to work as part of an overall wellness team. You may feel that this increases the effectiveness of counseling and enhances the entire wellness process.

_____ I want a counselor who is willing to confer with my other health care providers and who is willing to work as part of my health care team.

People in the study described what, for them, would be the ideal counselor. Check those that are important to you.

_____ respectful	_____ warm
_____ gives unconditional positive regard	_____ non-judgmental
_____ intelligent	_____ perceptive
_____ compassionate	_____ confrontative
_____ considerate	_____ professional
_____ consistent	_____ honest
_____ supportive	_____ a good listener
_____ gives good advice	_____ educates me
_____ confidential	_____ interested
_____ caring	_____ concerned

_____ provides referral to resources

_____ has experience working with people with issues similar to mine

_____ has experienced issues similar to mine

_____ has training in dealing with issues similar to mine

_____ coordinates with other health care providers

_____ knows the signs that I am starting to have mental health difficulties and knows what to do if these signs appear

Other attributes you would like your counselor to have:

_____

_____

_____

_____

Interview several therapists before making a commitment. Get recommendations on who to interview from your physician, other people who have issues similar to yours, health care organizations, friends, peers and supporters. Request a free initial interview to help in determining if this is the right counselor for you.

I am going to get recommendations on counselors to interview from:

_____

_____

_____

When you have several names of possible therapists, call and ask for an initial interview.

_____ I am going to ask the following counselors for interviews.

Therapist Interview Date/Results of Interview

_____

_____

_____

_____

_____

Issues you may want to address in the initial interview

_____ payment (deal with payment issues in this first meeting so it does not get in the way of your relationship)

_____ counselor's background and experience

_____ training focus

_____ accessibility between appointments

_____ availability of backup if counselor is not available

_____ willingness to confer with family members and supporters

_____ attitude about medication use

_____ your goals in counseling (your goals in counseling need to be clearly understood by both you and your counselor.)

_____ your expectations

Other issues you would like to discuss with the counselor in the initial interview.

_____

_____

_____

_____

_____You can use the form on the next page as a guide for your Counselor Interviews.

Prospective Counselor Interview Form

Name _____ Address _____

Phone _____

Cost _____ Payment Options _____

If associated with an agency, what is the agency? _____

What services does it provide in addition to counseling? _____

_____

Areas of Specialty _____

Education _____

Licenses or Accreditations _____

Experience _____

_____

Accessibility _____

Back-up Availability _____

Willingness to confer with other health care providers _____

Willingness to confer with family members or other supporters at your request _____

Willing to be part of a health care team _____

How did you feel about this counselor? _____-

_____

_____

Is this a person you would consider as your counselor? If so, why?

_____

_____

If not, why not?

_____

_____

If You Are in Counseling Now

Perhaps you are already seeing a counselor. You may want to use the following exercises to assess how the counseling is working for you.

____ I am in counseling now.

I deal with the following issues:

_____

_____

_____

_____

____ Counseling is working well for me because:

_____

_____

_____

_____

_____

____ Counseling is not helpful. If not, why not:

_____

_____

_____

_____

_____

What do you need from the counseling that you are not getting?

_____

_____

_____

_____

_____

How could you change this situation to make your counseling experience more effective?

_____

_____

_____

_____

_____

The right counselor feels right to you. No one else can choose your counselor for you. Some people are compatible for a counseling relationship and others are not.

I choose to begin counseling with _____.

The Counseling Session

There is no way to describe a typical counseling session. They vary as much as counselors and the people being counseled.

Expect the counseling session to be a safe place to be yourself and express thoughts, to receive guidance, reassurance and encouragement, to be supported, to get assistance in monitoring feelings and to learn how to help yourself.

You may feel that the focus of sessions tends to be on management and crisis control rather than exploration of issues which might be causing or exacerbating your issues. You may find this frustrating and be pleased when management and crisis control are no longer the focus of each session.

Descriptions of counseling from people who have experienced mental health difficulties:

I expect the counseling session to be a safe place to allow my self to feel my moods and express my thoughts. I expect guidance when I begin to get off track if I'm not aware of this or not allowing myself to acknowledge it. I expect reassurance and encouragement when I experience more depression, because it is too easy to begin feeling "things will never change." Counseling plays a vital role in helping me maintain my wellness. I realize that I must do the work and be responsible, but the counseling helps me gain more insight and awareness so that I can make better decisions when my mental health issues are affecting my thinking and feeling.

In counseling I just talk about what is bothering me. When I don't make myself clear the counselor asks questions. She gives me things to think about. I expect reinforcement for my way of thinking and available options that I can't think of.

I work just as hard as my counselor and fully understand that she does NOT have any magical powers or all the answers. This is a team effort. I discuss any issues of importance to me since my previous appointment. We discuss any significant changes in mood, medication as prescribed by my physician, and ways I've dealt with these things. Positive thinking is reinforced.

My counselor monitors my health through my charts, speaks with other physicians and I feel she really cares. Without counseling I would be lost with a lot of "boxed up old junk"! We talk about feelings that arise out of situations that I have experienced. She challenges my negative thoughts about myself. She lets me know when she sees changes in my behavior and gives me positive feedback on my progress.

The session content depends on how I feel and what I want to talk about. I expect my counselor to listen and be interested. If I did not go to counseling, I would still keep all these things inside of me and I know I can not do that anymore. If I did I would never get well.

I usually have an immediate problem I want to discuss, but sometimes the counselor initiates the talk. I expect it to help me discern if problems I have are real, or if my view of things is distorted. Ongoing contact between my counselor and doctor is really helpful.

You may want to take a list of issues to discuss to each session with your counselor.

_____ I am going to take a list of issues I want to discuss with my counselor to each session.

You may find it helpful to keep a journal that records the focus of counseling sessions, specific points to remember, and action that was decided upon. It also provides a useful record of progress. For instance, a counselor advised a woman to take afternoon naps so wouldn't be tired in the evening. The journal was a good place for her to keep track of her naps and how they made her feel.

Some counselors may suggest "homework," activities between sessions that will facilitate the counseling process, such as contacting a physician to ask questions about medication side effects. The journal is a good place to keep track of such activities.

_____ I am going to keep a journal related to my counseling.

Expect that counseling is going to be confined to the agreed-upon hour. Counselors have schedules that they need to follow.

Be strict in adherence to payment arrangements. The counselor is dependent on this money for their income. Lack of payment creates tension that can hamper your relationship with your counselor.

In counseling you can expect to be given ideas, choices and opportunities to search for the right answer or strategy. The counselor is there to help you discover what you need to do for yourself or understand about yourself in order to feel better.

Reserving Counseling Time to Work on Issues

Use your counseling session to work on important issues Don't allow the issues you discuss in counseling to take over and control your life.

When you leave the counseling session, leave these concerns behind and get on with the good things in your life. This does not mean you do not address and deal with issues. It just means you deal with issues in counseling, using the rest of your time to do what you need to do to manage your life and have a good time. Some of us visualize putting all our issues or troubles in a box and storing it away after each counseling session, bringing it out and re-examining the contents during those times reserved to work on such issues, when in a safe, supportive place.

Try this: Get into a comfortable position. Feel yourself settle into your chair, your back resting on the back of the chair, your feet firmly on the floor. Close your eyes. Take three deep breaths. Visualize a box. It can be a heavy wooden box or a strong metal box, it can be ornate or plain. Make sure it has a strong lock and you are the keeper of the key. As you review each issue that you discussed in your session, put it in the box. When you have put in all your issues, concerns, cares, and difficult memories, close the box and lock it. Visualize yourself locking the box and storing it on a high shelf in a special place. Make a promise to yourself not to take the box down or examine the contents until your next session. Now give yourself credit for a task well done. Slowly bring your attention back to the room.

End your counseling session by refocusing attention back to the good things that are currently happening in your life. Good questions are, "What are you looking forward to this week?" "What are you going to do to make yourself feel good this afternoon?" "What is your favorite way to spend an evening?" "What is your favorite outfit?" "Who would you most like to meet on the street when you leave here?" "Name two people who you would enjoy being in touch with this week?"

I find that it helps me to have a plan for what I am going to do right after a counseling session. Usually it is going to the health food store and getting a healthy but delicious treat or stopping at the florist to look at the flowers and choosing a special one for myself. Spending time chatting with a friend or shopping for groceries also helps to bring my focus back to the present.

List activities that will help focus your attention back on the present after a counseling session.

_____

_____

_____

_____

Counseling Length

People stay in counseling relationships from six months to "forever." Most people said they were in counseling several years. Counseling relationships have been a very important part of my overall treatment strategy. I have had two counselors for extended periods of time, the first for eight years. I am currently seeing a counselor who I have been seeing for over 20 years.

The length of time people spend in counseling varies according to individual need and, sadly, is often limited by financial considerations. Many health plans will not cover sessions, limit the number of counseling sessions, or have a cap on the amount of money that can be spent in a year or a lifetime on mental health-related services. Again, advocacy for appropriate coverage is needed.

The optimum for most people is to have a good counselor that they see on a regular basis for as long as necessary. When intensive counseling is no longer needed, the counselor could be available for occasional sessions. Given individual differences and the uncertainties of life, it is not possible to predict or recommend an appropriate length of counseling treatment.

Counseling That Was Not Helpful

Counseling is to benefit the person who is being counseled. You have the right to end the counseling or find a different counselor if you choose to, if it is making you feel worse, or it just doesn't feel right.

In one of my first counseling relationships, I worked with a counselor who was using an approach that involved excessive, inappropriate and critical interpretations of my feelings and actions. This made me feel less adequate and more depressed. Unfortunately, I thought that whatever the counselor said or did was right, and so I internalized the negativity. I was not yet able to look at the relationship objectively and understand that it was not helpful. Instead, I thought something was wrong with me.

In counseling you should not be:
- judged, blamed, criticized
- feeling like the counselor is better or more knowledgeable than you are
- told what to do
- forced to probe into areas and issues you are not ready to address
- encouraged to go to faster
- told you remember things you don't remember.

When any of the following are said to us, they don't help. If they are said to you, tell your counselor it was not helpful. If you are not satisfied with their response, you may need a different counselor.

- Just call the Center in the morning.

- You are just feeling sorry for yourself.

- Why are you so quiet?

- I know best.

- Pull yourself up by the bootstraps.

- It's all in your head.

- If you would just try harder, you could do it.

- Are you trying to hide something from me?

Caution

Beware the therapist or counselor who suggests, encourages, attempts, forces or claims any type of sexual contact to be necessary to the therapeutic process or relationship. Leave the relationship immediately. Do not see the counselor again under any circumstances. Report the person to the state licensing board or other body responsible for such matters in your area. If you do not know who to report to in your area, call your state office of protection and advocacy, a legal aid lawyer, or your attorney. A reputable counselor will never suggest or allow any type of sexual or inappropriate contact, or even contact that makes you feel uncomfortable.

People who are struggling with difficult life situations can fall prey to unscrupulous practitioners who are not making decisions or taking action in the best interests of their clients. Sexual contact with a trusted therapist is damaging and devastating.

Also be wary if the your therapist tells you to stop relationships with family members or friends or to trust them completely, if he or she threatens you in any way, tells you not to discuss your session with anyone else and/or offers protection from others.

Wellness and Recovery Strategies

Exchange Listening

I "exchange listen" every Friday afternoon with a good friend. It helps so much. I figure things out that I can't figure out any other way.

Many people have found exchange listening, a structured form of mutual attention and support, to be a valuable technique that gives you an opportunity to express yourself any way you choose, while supported by a trusted ally.

For some people, exchange listening is the key component of their wellness program. I have found that exchange listening, when used consistently, is a free, safe and effective self-help tool that encourages expression of feelings and emotions. It puts you in control of your own healing process. It is very useful in addressing issues or problems identified in the chapter, "Life Assessment."

All of us encounter a wide variety of situations that can be disturbing and, if not addressed, take away our vitality. If responses to past experiences, hurts, trauma, and misinformation, are not examined to determine their validity, and if the resulting emotions are not expressed, you may experience various mental health difficulties, including sadness, anxiety, fear, embarrassment, guilt, shame, low self-esteem, and lack of self confidence.

Exchange listening gives you a forum where you can carefully examine past experiences, hurts, trauma, and misinformation, and express emotions. It is based on the premise that you are fine, know what to do to heal yourself and can do what you need to do to heal yourself. You know, at some level, the solutions to your problems and the reality of your beliefs. Exchange listening helps you find those solutions and trust your beliefs. Everyone is born as an intelligent, loving, creative person with enthusiasm for life and its adventures. Life experiences divert us from this reality. Exchange listening reintroduces us to it.

In exchange listening, we look at information in light of present day reality, releasing emotion and correcting misinformation. For instance, because of the circumstances of my childhood, I have always felt that people didn't like me, especially those people I am close to. Through the exchange listening process, I discovered where these feelings came from, expressed emotion, and have begun to incorporate into my consciousness the truth, which is *people do like me, even when we are close.*

Exchange Listening Sessions

In an exchange listening session, two people spend a previously agreed-upon amount of time together, dividing the time equally, paying attention to each other's issues, needs, and distresses. Sessions usually last one hour but can be shorter or longer. Half of the time is spent addressing each person's issues while the other person pays attention.

Exchange listeners have an ongoing agreement to complete confidentiality. Judging, criticizing and giving advice are not allowed.

While many people prefer sessions where you meet in person, sessions can be held over the phone when necessary. Sessions take place in a comfortable, quiet atmosphere, where there will be no interruption or distraction, and where the session cannot be overheard by others. Disconnect the phone, turn off the radio and television, and do whatever is necessary to eliminate other distractions.

The content of the session is determined by the person who is receiving attention–the "talker." If you are this person, you can use your time any way you choose. It may include eager talk, tears, crying, trembling, perspiration, indignant storming, laughter, reluctant talk, yawning, shaking, singing, or punching a pillow. You may want to spend some time planning your life and your goals. The only thing that is not OK is being rude to, or hurting, the person who is listening or paying attention.

Most people find that exchange listening sessions are most effective if you focus on one issue. At the beginning of a session you may want to focus on one particular issue, but as you proceed, you may find other issues coming up that take precedence.

The person who is listening and paying attention (the "listener"), needs to do only that–be an attentive and supportive listener. The person who is paying attention must never demand anything of the other person. Full control must remain at all times with the person who is receiving attention.

The release of emotion around issues can be important to the process. This release can be facilitated if the listener encourages the person to repeat over and over a statement that contradicts erroneous belief patterns. Only do this if it is all right with the "talker." For instance, in dealing with my low self-confidence, the person listening to me encouraged me to repeat "I have the ability to do whatever I need to do." After repeating this several times (or many times) I start to cry or laugh, releasing emotion around the issue. After releasing the emotion, I always feel much better. I have done this repeatedly in exchange listening, working on a wide variety of issues.

Some issues take only a session or two to resolve. Others will be ongoing for a long time.

In exchange listening, the release of emotion is <u>never</u> seen as a "symptom" or a sign that "you are mentally ill ," need a diagnosis or need to take medication. The release of emotion can be a vital part of the wellness process. In the past, you may have been treated badly and even hospitalized for expressing emotion. You may have learned not to release emotion because it did not feel safe. This can interfere with your wellness process. My mother was first taken to a mental hospital because she spent many days crying. As I look back, I wonder if her life had gotten overwhelming and she needed a good long crying session. Some people reported that they were warned by other patients in psychiatric facilities to avoid the release of emotion, as it would lengthen their hospital stay, or penalties would be incurred against them. It took me a long time to feel safe expressing emotion, even in the exchange listening setting.

A woman who has experienced mental health difficulties for many years said: "When I am depressed, I choose to seek out someone who will listen to me without trying to "fix" me or "change" me or "take care of me ," someone who will listen to my "crazy" thoughts without telling me "You're wrong ," "You're overreaching, etc." Sometimes just saying my fears out loud dispels them. My friend just held me while I cried last night. I appreciate someone allowing me to cry in their presence."

The person who is receiving attention can make requests of the other person to assist in the process such as:

Tell me what you like about me.

Hold me.

Pretend you are _____ (parent, child, peer, employer, friend, etc.) so I can safely tell that person how I feel or practice telling that person how I feel or what I want.

Some people feel that, because they are having a difficult time in their own life, they can only listen or share for a short time. Honor those feelings, increasing the length of sessions as it feels right to do so.

Occasionally the "listener" will feel that the other person has so much to work on or is having a such hard time that they should relinquish their time to be heard. This is not a good idea. Those of us who exchange listen have found that sessions without mutual sharing are not effective. Everyone needs time to listen as well as be heard. If a person cannot listen at a session, arrange time when they will be available to listen.

Sometimes people find that three-way or group exchange listening is helpful. The time is divided equally between the participants. When you are receiving attention, you are receiving it from several people instead of one. This can be very validating. It also means you have to listen to all of the other people share. Think carefully about this before you agree to it.

You may never have never received attention to your issues, concerns and feelings. When sharing with a person committed to paying close attention, it is amazing what can be accomplished.

I have always had low self-confidence that contributes to my depression. When I become aware that I am beginning to feel depressed, it is usually feelings of low self-confidence that are intruding. I have several friends with whom I exchange listen regularly. I have addressed this issue repeatedly in the exchange listening sessions. After the sessions I feel a great sense of relief. When those thoughts begin to intrude and become obsessive, I arrange another exchange listening session. I feel I have made significant progress through regularly scheduled weekly exchange listening sessions, with additional sessions set up on an as-needed basis. If I obsess in my mind about my lack of self-confidence, feelings of depression deepen.

If you are feeling badly, are in a crisis or if it just feels like the right thing to do, ask the peer listeners you work with for additional sessions. Have several listeners that you work with so there is always one available when needed. They can be the same people that are on your list of supporters. See the Chapter 3, "Support."

See "Steps for Exchange Listening" at the end of this chapter.

Focusing Attention on the Present

When mental health difficulties are making you feel uncomfortable and keeping you from doing the things you need to do, and the things you enjoy doing, it is best to focus exchange listening sessions on getting things back in order in one's life and to focus away from past issues. For instance, if you are feeling sad or anxious because your relationship, housing and work situations are uncertain and unstable, you may benefit from having the opportunity to explore choices and make decisions while feeling safe and supported. Using the session to address and resolve these immediate problems, in this case, can be more helpful than focusing on past issues.

Keep the counseling session contained, so that time outside counseling can be used to do things that make you feel good and to manage responsibilities. The session can be kept contained by the following activities:

1. At the beginning of a session, the listener reinforces the good that is happening in a person's life by asking them to share three good things that have happened in the last week (or day, or month, etc.). This also provides a starting point for the session.

Three good things I shared with a listener in a recent session:

1. Over 60 people attended a workshop I presented in Alaska.

2. I took a fun walk with my daughter and we watched birds and looked for shells.

3. I saw four bald eagles today.

2. At the conclusion of the session, the listener brings the other person back to focus on the present by asking the person a benign or even silly question. The question can be a nonsense or wrong answer question.

Sample questions:

What are computers for?

What color do you like the least?

What do you use couch cushions for?

Where do you think the car that just went by is going?

What do people wear hats for?

Who is the most important person in the world?

At the end of a session (or anytime it is appropriate), it is useful to remind yourself to stay in the present by repeating the following affirmation:

I don't have time to focus on difficult issues. There are many things I would rather do such as going for a walk, playing with my child, reading a good book, watching a humorous video, petting the cat, making bread, or painting a picture.

Make a list of things you would rather do than focus on difficult issues (this can be a very long list):

_____

_____

_____

_____

_____

You may find that it is very difficult to focus your attention away from problems and issues when you are not exchange listening. Ongoing reminders can facilitate the process. Until focusing your attention off your problems becomes a positive habit, you may need to remind yourself. Say to yourself, the following, whenever you find yourself thinking about difficult issues:

I am going to stop thinking about my problems and instead I will _____

_____.

You may have to remind yourself almost every moment to stay focused on the present outside of exchange listening sessions and when you are not using other techniques such as counseling, focusing and journaling to deal with issues. But you will feel so much better when you do.

Don't be critical of yourself if this is hard for you. It is very hard for most people. It will improve with consistent practice.

Intensive Exchange Listening

Occasionally some people feel the need for longer, more intensive exchange listening sessions-several hours, a day or more–with listeners taking turns giving and receiving attention.

A young woman was hospitalized for symptoms that might be described as mania. Some time after her release from the hospital, she was again beginning to have those same feelings-agitation, lack of sleep, and racing thoughts. She arranged around-the-clock exchange listening sessions, exchange listening for four days. The "manic episode" subsided. She has not taken psychiatric medications or been hospitalized since that time. She is now a highly effective and respected teacher and mother.

Another woman said:
I share time one hour each week with a fellow employee, providing mutual support. In addition, we talk whenever we want. This is a valuable time for both of us. It is helpful to have an understanding person to share things with. It gives immediate support if needed–confidential, understanding and encouraging.

Record Keeping

If exchange listening is an essential component of your wellness program, you may want to keep notes on various aspects of each session, as a way of keeping track of progress and reminding yourself of issues to address.

A spiral notebook can be used, or the form that follows can be copied and clipped together for an ongoing record of your progress and experience. You could also keep this record on your computer.

Exchange listening Record

Date _____ Counseled with _____ Length of Session _____

Issues Discussed _____

_____

_____

Comment _____

_____

_____

_____

_____

How I felt before the session _____

_____

_____

How I felt after the session _____

_____

_____

Next exchange listening session Date _____ Time _____
Place _____ With whom _____

Basic Exchange Listening Instructions

Ask someone you feel comfortable with to Exchange Listen with you.

Agree on how often you will share time together and the amount of time you will be together.

Find a place where you will not be disturbed.

As talker, start your time by sharing something that happened in the past week that you enjoyed. End your time by sharing something you are looking forward to, or answering a question posed by the talker.

As talker, use your time any way you want to, talking, laughing, yelling, crying, singing, trembling, whatever feels right to you. Focus on issues that seem most important to you.

If you are sharing beliefs or feelings that you know are erroneous, ask the listener to help you figure out contradictory statements that you might say instead. For instance, if you keep saying "I am no good ," you might change it to, "I am good" or "I am great."

As listener, give your complete attention to the person who is sharing, letting them know by nodding your head, and other body language, that you are paying close attention. Do not interrupt them unless they ask you a question or request your assistance.

Exchange listening is the most important part of my wellness program. When I exchange listen often, I feel more satisfied with my life.

Wellness and Recovery Strategies

Focusing

So simple, yet so important and helpful.

Focusing is a simple, safe, free, non-invasive, yet powerful self-help technique that was brought to my attention by friends in England. They report that this method is commonly used there successfully to relieve those feelings that can escalate into serious mental health difficulties. Based on this strong recommendation, I attended a Focusing workshop. It was led by Dr. Neil Friedman, a student of Eugene Gendlin, founder of this method, who teaches and writes on Focusing.

Once I had basic instruction in this technique, I began my own regular practice of Focusing. Whenever things felt too busy, confused or hectic, I found myself a comfortable space and went through the steps of a Focusing exercise. It helped! Instead of feeling so "scattered," I got a sense of what was really bothering me. And with that "focus" came a shift or change in the way I felt. The shift or change was sometimes slight and sometimes profound. Either way, it made me feel relieved and more stable. Often the insight included ideas on the next step or steps that could be taken to rectify the situation.

I left sessions calm, relaxed and with a clear sense of direction. I used Focusing when I had been "Triggered," when I had "Early Warning Signs" and even "When Things were Breaking Down." It worked so well. In some cases the feelings evoked were profound. At other times they were simpler and gentler. I now include "Focusing" in my growing repertoire of important Wellness Tools that, used regularly, increase my level of wellness and enhance my life.

The Focusing sequence, using a series of well-defined questions or steps, helps you focus on the "real" issue of most importance at a given time, not what you may be thinking "should" be the real issue. It then connects you with the feelings generated by that issue. When connection with the feelings are made and explored, a positive change in feeling is often achieved. The result is understanding at a new level that translates into feeling better.

You may find Focusing difficult at first. You may not be familiar with deliberately working with yourself in this way. With daily practice it becomes easier. It is also easier if you have a teacher when you are learning this technique. Information on teachers in your area is available through the Focusing Institute, listed at the end of this chapter.

In doing Focusing, you may have difficulty with differentiating between physical feelings like a queasy stomach or an aching back, and the physical "feeling sense" that occurs with a change in our perception or understanding of problems and issues. This becomes easier with practice.

Focusing is something like meditation, but it is not meditation. Meditation is an effective quieting and healing process in which you clear yourself out, empty yourself and give yourself a chance to just be. In "Focusing," you think, respond and feel.

The best way to gain a clear understanding of Focusing is to try it. Following are three sets of Focusing instructions. Use the one that feels right to you or use them as a guide in developing your own set of Focusing instructions.

The Focusing process is extremely safe and can be used by anyone. You are completely in charge of your own process and you need only pursue a direction of your choice.

Focusing Instructions #1

Have a person you trust, and with whom you feel safe, slowly read you the following instructions, taking the time between each step to follow the instructions in your mind and body. If no one is available to read the instructions to you, record the instructions, again allowing space for action, and play it back to yourself. Over time you will get to know the instructions and will easily think them through. This makes Focusing a readily accessible tool in almost all situations and circumstances.

1. Make yourself comfortable. Lie down, or sit on a comfortable chair. Loosen clothing that is restrictive. Take several deep breaths and allow yourself to relax fully.

2. How are you feeling? How are you? What's between you and feeling fine? Don't answer; let what comes in your body do the answering. Several issues may come up. Don't go into anything. Greet each concern that comes. Put each aside in your memory, acknowledging but not addressing it. Then ask yourself, "Except for these things, am I fine?"

3. Review the list of things that stand between you and feeling fine. Which one stands out the most, seems the most important, is having the most effect on how you are feeling? Choose that problem to focus on. Don't go into the problem. What do you sense in your body when you think about all aspects of that problem? Feel all of it. Where do you feel it in your body? What does it feel like?

4. What is the quality of that feeling? What one word , phrase, or image comes out of that feeling? What quality word , image, memory, music, or poetry fits it best? Take several minutes to explore the possibilities, and find the one that feels right.

5. Go back and forth between the word or image and the feeling. Do they match? If they don't quite fit together, explore further until you come up with the right word or image. When it feels like they match, let your attention go back and forth from the feeling to the word or image several times. Let yourself feel that for a minute or two–whatever feels right to you.

6. Ask yourself, "What is it about the problem that makes me feel so _____ (word or image) ?" Let the answer come to you. If an answer doesn't come easily, ask yourself, *What is the worst of this feeling? What's really so bad about this? What does it need? What should happen?* Don't answer; wait for the feeling to stir and give you an answer. Now ask yourself, "What would it feel like if it was all OK?" "What is in the way of feeling that?"

7. Feel the change in your feelings that comes from having this new-felt information. Welcome and feel the feelings and information that comes to you. Know that it is only one step in dealing with this problem, not the last. Now that you know where it is, you can leave it and come back to it later. Don't analyze it or criticize it.

8. Ask your body if it wants another round of Focusing, or is this a good stopping place? If it wants another round of Focusing, and you have the time, go through the steps again.

Focusing Instructions #2

Have a person you trust, and with whom you feel safe, slowly read you the following instructions, allowing time between each step to follow the instructions in your mind and body. If no one is available, record the instructions, again allowing space for action, and play it to yourself.

1. Get into a comfortable position, either sitting, or lying on the floor. Take a few deep breaths, relax and close your eyes.

2. Ask yourself, "How do I feel inside right now?" Imagine a searchlight, searching through your body, finding places that feel good and places where tension exists.

3. Ask, "What is keeping me from feeling fine right now?" Let whatever comes up, come up. Imagine a stack of your problems or feelings, with you some distance away from them.

4. Choose one problem to work on right now, the one that seems to stand out or demand the most attention.

5. Focus on what that one thing feels like, how it makes you feel inside your body.

6. Find a word, phrase, sound, gesture or image that fits the feeling while you are feeling it.

7. Say the sound, word, phrase, gesture back to yourself–over and over. See if it matches the feeling. If it doesn't feel right, try another until you find one that fits.

8. Keeping your attention on the feelings, ask words, images or memories to come from the feeling itself. Now exhale what you received.

9. Ask yourself the following questions, taking deep breathes between each questions
    a. What is the core of the feeling? What is it about? (Answer with your body, not your head.)
    b. What's wrong?
    c. What's the worst of this feeling?
    d. What does this feeling need?
    e. What is a good small step in the right direction for this thing?
    f. What needs to happen?
    g. What would my body feel like if this thing were all cleared up? Allow yourself to feel how that would feel.
    h. Ask yourself, " What is exactly the right question to ask at this time?" Now let yourself respond, not with your head, but with your feelings.

10. Use the next minute to stretch, and relax then to open your eyes and come back to the present.

11. Do another round of Focusing if it feels right to do so at this time.

____ I am going to try Focusing. Why?

_____
_____
_____
_____

____ I am not going to try Focusing. Why not?

_____
_____
_____
_____

Describe your Focusing session.

You might like to keep written records of your Focusing sessions in a journal. This will allow you to review a sequence of sessions over time and get a sense of your accomplishment. It also reinforces the results of your sessions.

You can use the following format as a guide to recording your sessions.

Person who read instructions _____

I listened to my recording of the instructions _____

I went through the steps in my mind _____

How did you feel before you focused?

_____
_____
_____
_____

What issues came up for you when you were Focusing?

_____
_____Which issue did you focus

on? _____

Describe the feelings that came with this issue.

_____
_____
_____What word or image resonated with

these feelings? _____
Describe changes in feeling that occurred in the session.

_____
_____
_____

If there are any, describe any changes you are going to take as a result of this session.

_____
_____

How did you feel after the session?

_____

_____

_____Did the instructions as given work well for

you? _____ If not, how would you change them to better meet your needs?

_____

_____

_____

_____

_____

Focusing would have been more effective if a different person had read the instructions _____yes

_____no

Why? _____

Next time I would choose to focus with _____

Why? _____

The recording worked very well _____yes _____no

Why? _____

Next time I would _____

Going through the steps in my mind worked very well _____yes _____no

Next time I would _____

Why? _____

Focusing Instructions #3

You may focus so much on problems and issues that you never get a sense of "feeling good."
Enhance the positive experiences in your life through Focusing. They deserves attention as well.

Try Focusing using the following questions.

1. Make yourself comfortable. Do whatever is necessary to make your self comfortable. Lie down
or sit on a comfortable chair. Loosen clothing that is restrictive. Take several deep breaths and
allow yourself to relax fully.

2. How are you feeling? How are you? What's making you feel good? Don't answer; let what
comes in your body do the answering. Several things may come up. Don't go into anything. Greet
each good thing that comes. Put each aside in your memory, acknowledging but not addressing.
Are all of these the things that are making you feel fine?

2. Review the list of things that are making you feel good . Which one stands out the most, seems the most important, is having the most effect on how you are feeling? Choose that to focus on. Don't go into it. What do you sense in your body when you think about all aspects of this good thing? Feel all of it. Where do you feel it in your body? What does it feel like?

3. What is it about this whole thing that makes you so (give it a word or an image)?

4. What is the best of this feeling?

5. How did you create this originally to bring this (word, image) to you?

6. What does this feeling need from you in order to stay, or be with you more often? Or what does it need from you to be there when you want it?

7. What is the next step in this? Can your body let you feel the next step in this progression? (if appropriate)

8. Review the process you have just been through and ask for an action step.

9. See how this makes you feel. Ask yourself what is in the way of feeling like this more often.

10. Ask yourself if you should do another round of Focusing or if it is time to move on to other activities.

You may want to use the following questions as a guide to writing about your experience.

How did you feel before Focusing on a positive issue?

_____

_____

_____

_____

_____

What good things came up for you when you were Focusing?

_____

_____

_____

_____

Which good thing did you focus on? _____

Describe the feelings that came with this good thing.

_____

_____

_____

What word or image resonated with these feelings? _____

Describe changes in feeling that occurred in the session.

_____

_____

_____

_____

If there are any, describe any small steps you are going to take as a result of this session.

_____

_____

_____

How did you feel after the session?

_____

_____

_____

Did the instructions as given work well for you? _____ If not, how would you change them?

_____

_____

_____

_____

Additional Ideas That May Enhance Your Focusing Experience

You may find it helpful to think of a special, quiet, private, comfortable and convenient place, and reserve it for Focusing.

I am going to focus (where) because _____

_____

If you haven't tried Focusing, and you find this technique intriguing, attend a Focusing workshop. You can find out where one is by looking up "Focusing" on the internet.

References

Gendlin, E. *Focusing*. New York: Bantam Books, 1981.

This inexpensive book enhances understanding of the effectiveness of Focusing. It also provides an excellent guide to learning Focusing.

Wellness and Recovery Strategies

Journaling

My diary–my journal — is my best friend. It has seen me through the worst and the best of times.

People have kept diaries and accounts of activities, events and feelings since the beginning of time. Recently we have become more aware of the power of this tool in dealing with various kinds of mental health issues. You have only to look to the popularity of workbook-style self-help books to become aware of the value of writing to release pent-up emotions and to help you find solutions to problems.

In moments of ecstasy, in moments of despair, the journal remains an impassive, silent friend, forever ready to coach, to confront, to critique, to console. Its potential as a tool for holistic mental health is unsurpassed. (Adams, K. Journal to the Self. New York: Warner Books, 1990).

The kind of deep inner exploration and evaluation that the journaling process encourages is a valuable asset to the wellness process and a wonderful and popular Wellness Tool.

Why Journal?

The following quotes are from a few of the many people who have gotten well, and stayed well, using journal writing as a key part of their wellness process.

"It affirms and validates me to keep a chronology of my life."

"Journal writing is fun and it feels really good."

"My journal is always available. It is a completely trusted friend when no one else is around."

"My counselor suggested I keep a journal of our work together. It makes the counseling process easier and more effective for me."

"I like journaling because I don't need to depend on anyone else to do it and no one else is telling me what to do."

"I use my journal to monitor changes in the way I feel."

"When I write, it helps keep me from internalizing negative thoughts."

"It helps me to get my anger and pain out from inside of me and onto the paper."

"Journal writing leaves a trail of my thinking–reflections to return to."

"When I opened my journal to 1989 and reflected on where I was at that time, I was awed by the progress I have made. My journal has also helped me chart my behaviors and feelings during seasonal changes."

"I use journal writing in my wellness process. It allows me to let go of the day's stresses. I begin by writing whatever thought comes first, and then I write how I feel–not just about the thought, but how I feel about how I feel–and go on from there–writing everything that comes to my head."

"My journal has helped me get over my addiction to food. When I feel like munching, and know I have had plenty to eat, I write in my journal instead."

"I can express any emotion I want while writing, without being criticized or judged."

"After my psychotic episodes, I had to learn to write again. My thoughts would not come out correctly. I would have to rewrite my thoughts many times before they lost their being all jumbled. Through regular writing in my journal, this skill has improved greatly."

"When I was very ill and first out of the hospital, I used journaling to express my thoughts and feelings because it was very difficult to verbalize them. This also helped me when talking with my psychiatrist. When I received therapy from him, it was a way to share my experience and a way to begin sessions when it was difficult to talk."

"My journal is a safe place to let go of feelings I can't vent in other ways."

I have had an ongoing journal since I was a child. I have written on everything from the back of junk mail to lovely cloth-bound diaries. Most of my recent writings are on the computer. I print them out and keep them in a folder. My "journals" are stacked on a shelf in my closet.

Sometimes I write daily. At other times my journal writing has taken a vacation of several months. When I feel drawn to my journal, I again pick up the pen and begin. Now I look back, impressed with all the writing I have done, how my life has changed over the years and realize how important this tool is to me.

For about a month I had very high energy, the kind of feeling that precedes what might be called a "manic episode." It seemed to be related to reminders and recurring memories of old abuse issues. I would wake every morning at 3 AM and be unable to get back to sleep. I kept my journal beside my bed . When I woke up, I wrote and wrote and wrote. Soon I would get tired and go back to sleep. In that time I worked through some very important issues. It was a very healing process.

During a long hospitalization, a journal was the only thing I could relate to. I wrote, almost non-stop for days. It is the most valuable writing I have ever done. The process of all that "stuff" pouring out was clearing and cathartic. The hospital staff was encouraging and kept me supplied with notebooks. They respected my process and didn't interrupt my writing to go to meetings or classes. When I had poured out all I needed to, I felt very relieved and much better.

_____ I keep a journal. Why?

_____

_____

_____

Describe my experience of journaling _____

_____

_____

What role has journaling played in my wellness?

_____

_____

_____

_____ I am going to continue my relationship with my journal.

_____ I am going to start journaling.

What I Need to Begin Journaling

Paper-Use whatever paper is available and whatever feels right to you. Choices range from the backs of old envelopes and mail, to simple pads of paper, computer paper and spiral notebooks, to bound journals with fancy covers. Many people like to honor their journaling process by purchasing a specially made journal with an attractive cover. I have a fantasy of a very large journal, perhaps three feet high and two feet wide in which I could write to my heart's content while laying on my belly on the floor.

I am going to use _____ as my journal.

Writing instrument- Use whatever feels right to you—a pencil, magic marker, ball point pen, fountain pen, crayon, brush, or computer. Some people like to honor their journaling process by reserving a special writing implement for journaling, such as a pen with colored ink, or a fountain pen like they used in school.

I am going to use _____ to write in my journal.

One "journaler" said, "It's the cheapest kind of therapy—all you need is paper and something to write with."

A place to keep your journal- Have a safe, private space to store your journal, like in the bottom of your underwear drawer or on a high shelf. Other people in your household should respect your right to a private journal. I keep my journal on my night stand for easy accessibility if I awaken in the middle of the night.

If the privacy of your journal cannot be assured, you may want a trusted friend to keep your journal for you. In this case, you may want to use a binder. Keep a supply of paper on hand, write when you feel like it, and take the pages to your friend to include in your binder at another time.

I am going to keep my journal (where) _____.

Journaling Rules

This is easy. There are no rules.

Get some paper and a writing tool and start to write. Write anything you want, anything you feel. It doesn't have to make sense. It doesn't have to be real. It doesn't need to be interesting. It's all right to repeat yourself over and over. Whatever is written is for your value only. This is yours. You don't have to worry about punctuation, grammar, spelling, penmanship, neatness or staying on the lines. You can scribble all over the page if that makes you feel better. I have done that and it made me feel great, a wonderful way to get rid of tension.

Choosing to share writings is a personal choice. It is strictly your choice. The privacy of the journal should not be violated. You don't have to share your writings with anybody unless you want to. Some people find it helpful and feel comfortable to share writings with family members, friends, or health care providers. This is a personal choice.

You may want to set aside a time every day for journaling, but it is not necessary. Spend as little or as much time writing as you want. Some people like to set a timer so they know when to stop without ongoing time checks.

You can write in your journal anytime: daily, several times a day, weekly, before you go to bed, when you wake up, after supper, whenever you feel like it. The choice is yours.

You don't have to commit to keeping a journal for the rest of your life. Use your journal when you feel like it.

You can write at any speed you want, fast or slow. You can write as much or as little as you want.

You can write poems, paragraphs, verse, novels, novellas, fiction, reality, your autobiography, someone else's biography, wishes, fantasies, dreams, beliefs, loves, hates, etc., etc., etc. It can be similar each time or very different.

Suggestions

Write your name, address and phone number inside the front cover if you carry your journal with you. Add a statement something like this: "This contains private information. Please do not read it without my permission. Thank you!"

Some people like to quiet down before starting to journal. You can do this by taking several deep breaths and then Focusing on something pleasant for a moment or two (or as long as you want), such as a flower, a piece of fruit, your pet, or the view out the window. You might want to take a warm bath or go for a short walk, whatever quiets you down.

Claim a quiet space to journal, turn off the phone, and ask others to respect your need for quiet and privacy. Moms and dads may choose to journal when the baby is napping, the children are in school, or after the children have gone to bed.

You may want to choose a special place in your home that you decorate and reserve for journal writing. Lighting candles may feel good. I sometimes like to write in my journal by candlelight. Writing outside sitting under a big special tree or on the beach in the warm sunshine also feels good. Consider journaling while listening to your favorite music.

Date your entries if you want to. It helps to keep things in perspective as you review what you have written over time.

Don't fix your mistakes. Just keep writing. Draw or paste pictures or words in your journal. Doodle.

You may choose to keep your journal writings. Most people do. Others discard them. I have a friend who burned all her old journals as a way of celebrating an extended period of wellness. She said she needed to start anew.

Write quickly. Don't think too much about what you are writing, just let the writing flow.

Journaling Goals

If you are thinking about using journaling as one of your Wellness Tools, you may want to write some journaling goals to get started, but only if you want to. This could be your first journaling session.

Some possible journaling goals:
- to understand why I feel sad sometimes
- to understand why I feel frustrated and anxious sometimes
- to keep of track of how I feel
- to work on issues that have been getting in the way of feeling well
- to help understand life issues that affect the way I feel
- to guide me on a journey to recovery and wellness
- to enhance my understanding of myself
- to help in achieving my life goals
- to get to know myself better
- to write my own personal history
- to facilitate the counseling process
- to keep a record of counseling, exchange listening, Focusing or other activities
- to improve relationships
- to get over a relationship
- to grieve a loss
- to assist in problem solving
- to develop spontaneity
- for a deeper understanding of issues
- for a deeper understanding of others
- to explore dreams

- to pinpoint and address stressors
- to get in touch with feelings
- to become more comfortable writing
- to explore different aspects of my personality, different parts of myself
- to discover the good things in my life
- to keep track of life changes and growth
- just for the fun of it
- to safely work through feelings
- to explore creativity
- to enhance creativity
- to re-evaluate beliefs and behaviors
- to give myself credit for my progress

List your journaling goals, if you want to:

_____

_____

_____

_____

_____

_____

Journaling Exercises

If you have had a hard time starting to journal, you can use some of the following questions as a way to get started.

If my life could be any way that I want, what would it be like?

_____

_____

_____

_____

_____

_____

What do I like about myself?

_____

_____

_____

_____

_____

_____

What is making me feel good today?

_____

_____

_____

_____

_____

What made me feel sad today?

_____

_____

_____

_____

_____

What made me feel anxious today?

_____

_____

_____

_____

_____

What are the stressors in my life?

_____

_____

_____

_____

What makes me happy?

_____

_____

_____

_____

_____

_____

My favorite people are:

_____

_____

_____

_____

_____

_____

What makes me feel so good when I spend time with _____

_____

_____

_____

_____

_____

Journaling Activities

Write a letter to someone you would like to tell off but it wouldn't be wise or who is not available.

_____

_____

_____

_____

_____

Write a letter to yourself, pretending you are your own best friend.

_____

_____

_____

_____

_____

_____

List the best things that have happened this day (month, year, in your life)

_____
_____
_____
_____
_____
_____

The best thing that ever happened to me was:

_____
_____
_____
_____
_____
_____

The worst thing that ever happened to me was:

_____
_____
_____
_____
_____
_____

Make a list of all the reasons you want to be alive

_____
_____
_____
_____
_____

Write five things you need to do today and how you feel about doing them.

_____
_____
_____
_____
_____

Other ideas for journaling:

    Take an inventory of your life.

    Write your own prayer.

    Write yourself a question and then answer it.

    My ideal place to live would be:

    My ideal place to work would be:

    If I had one day left to live, I would:

    I am proud of myself because:

    Describe yourself.

    Describe someone else.

    Describe a special moment.

    Write a dialogue with another person, event, or thing.

    Dialogue with a part of your body.

    Dialogue with a famous person.

Make lists, like list of things you want to do in your life, why you like yourself, why you like someone else, why you feel stressed, why you want to be alive, fears, reasons to stay with your partner, reasons to have a child, reasons not to have a child, losses, things to do when depressed, things to do when manic, things I would never do again, what make me laugh, what makes me cry, what makes me happy, what makes me sad, my favorite people.

How do you feel about journaling?

_____

_____

_____

_____

_____

_____ I am going to start journaling because:

_____

_____

_____

_____ I am not going to start journaling because:

_____

_____

_____

_____

You can find lots of journaling resources on the internet. Several books that have stood the test of time are:

Adams, K. *Journal to the Self.* New York: Warner Books, 1990.

Baldwin, Christina. (1991) *Life's Companion: Journal Writing as a Spiritual Quest.* New York: Bantam Books, 1991.

Wellness and Recovery Strategies

Boosting Self-Esteem

If only I felt good about myself, I know I would feel so much better.

Low self-esteem and self-confidence are chronic, serious, personal issues that exist at epidemic proportions in today's society. Many people describe the limiting effects of negative self perceptions on their daily life, attainment of their life goals, and on their overall stability and wellness. These feelings seem to persist, even after they have been well for a long time.

Serious mental health difficulties, long term inability to meet responsibilities, and trouble getting anything done, along with guilt from possible actions and behaviors, can worsen already low self-esteem.

The methods described in this chapter for raising self-esteem and self-confidence are safe for anyone to use. However, people who have been victims of physical, emotional or sexual abuse, who were severely oppressed, or the victims of violent crime, may need the assistance of a counselor or involvement in a special program for people with post traumatic stress syndrome in order to regain a positive sense of their own value. Learn more about this kind of work by referring to the chapter on "Trauma."

Raising self-esteem is often very difficult and takes a long time. Negative thoughts about yourself, especially when they have been reinforced by others in your childhood, are very deeply ingrained. I have been working at raising my self-esteem and self-confidence for many years. I find that when I am under a lot of stress, my self-esteem drops. I counter that drop in self-esteem by using the kinds of activities described in this chapter.

Low self-esteem and lack of self-confidence come from many sources. Many people tend to blame their parents. And in fact, many parents, who were never taught good parenting skills, may have contributed to this problem. Parenting classes in our schools might help remedy this problem. However, there are many other sources of low self-esteem, that come from all sectors of our society, including educational institutions, the media, the work place, social and religious institutions, peer relationships, personal relationships, health care facilities, labeling practices, stigma, and prejudice. The antidote to this is for each person to have a strong sense of individual worth which is not dependent on others or society for its maintenance.

How do you feel about yourself right now? _____

_____

_____

_____

_____

How self confident are you? _____

_____

_____

_____

How would you like to feel about yourself? _____

_____

_____

_____

_____

Quick and Easy Ways to Feel Better

Use the following activities to give your self-esteem a boost. Incorporate one or several of the following activities into your daily schedule each day, especially on those days when you are feeling very low or down on yourself.

1. Do something you enjoy that you know makes you feel better about yourself. (fixing something, cleaning your space, painting a picture, taking a walk, playing a musical instrument, singing, reading a light novel, going to a good movie, etc.)
What do you enjoy doing?

_____

_____

_____

_____

2. Do something that makes you laugh (watching sitcoms on television, watching a funny video, reading a comedy that you find funny, getting together with a friend who has a good sense of humor, etc.) List the possibilities here.

_____

_____

_____

3. Do something nice for yourself. Buy yourself a gift or a flower. Light a candle to yourself. Give yourself a massage. Take an afternoon off to read a good book. Allow yourself time to watch a gorgeous sunset. What nice things could you do for yourself? _____

_____

_____

_____

_____

4. Do something special for someone else. Read a child a story, shop for a sick friend, send an "I'm Thinking About You" card to someone special, buy a friend an unexpected gift, volunteer at the local hospital, etc. List things you could do for someone else that would help you to feel better about yourself. _____

_____

_____

_____

5. Pretend you are your own best friend. If you were your own best friend, what would you tell "you" about yourself (take good care of yourself, eat right, do something fun, give your body needed nourishment and care, you are a great person, I love you, etc).

_____

_____

_____

_____

6. Make a list of your accomplishments in a day, a week, a month or in your life. Don't leave things out and give yourself credit for whatever you have done, not as compared to anyone else. Don't forget what might be considered "small" accomplishments like learning to tie your shoes and feeding your dog everyday.

_____

_____

_____

_____

_____

_____

Post the list in a prominent place. Then read it every time you start to get down on yourself.

7. Set up a space to honor yourself, a bureau top, a wall, the refrigerator door. Then fill the space with pictures of yourself, cards from people who care about you and other mementos. Spend a few minutes a day reviewing the contents of that space. Change the items as you feel like it.

I use the top of my dresser for this purpose. I have pictures of myself and special people in my life, trinkets I enjoy, gifts, cards and dried flowers.

I am going to set up a place to honor myself (where) _____

I am going to include in the space:

_____

_____

_____

_____

_____

8. Have pictures of yourself in prominent view around your living space. When you walk by each one, tell yourself something good about yourself.

I filled a frame with pictures of myself at different ages. I included a special quote from a supportive friend. I have it hanging at the top of the stairs where I have to look at it each time I go up or down the stairs. It constantly reminds me of how special I am.

____ I am going to hang a picture of pictures of myself in prominent places around my living space. My plan to do this includes:

_____

_____

_____

_____

_____

9. Look at a child. Think of all the good things you would like to tell that child about her/ or himself. Then tell yourself the same things.

Through my life I have looked back on my childhood and said to myself, "Why didn't you do this or that?" "Why didn't you keep your room neat like your sister did?" "Why didn't you try harder in school?" I also had the habit of obsessing about things I did that were embarrassing to me, like running into a parked car with my bicycle when waving to an elderly friend on a porch.

One day last year I was walking by a school playground. I saw lots of little boys and girls at play. I thought to myself, "You would never judge those children in the harsh way that you judge yourself as a child." From that time on I have been much more compassionate with my thoughts about myself as a child. It has translated into better feelings about myself.

Using only positive references, describe yourself as a child:

_____

_____

_____

_____

_____

10. Get together with a trusted friend. Divide a block of time in half, for instance, 20 minutes divided in half would be 10 minutes each. Then take turns telling the other person everything good about them. Just think, 10 minutes of compliments.

The first time I tried that exercise I found it was very easy to give the other person compliments, but very difficult to hear compliments directed at me. I have made it a point to get used to sharing compliments and having that make me feel good. See the chapter "Exchange Listening."

____ I am going to try the compliment sharing exercise with _____ .

11. Ask for what you want and need for yourself. Advocate for yourself. Don't allow anyone to treat you badly. Don't allow your self to be a victim! Be your own best friend! You deserve it! See the chapter "Self Advocacy."

What do you need for yourself now? Is it a better housing situation, better treatment on the job, help with chores from family members, attention from health care providers?

What I need?

_____

_____

_____

How I am going to get it:

_____

_____

_____

12. Have a celebration. Celebrate that you got up, made the bed, worked every day this week or one day this week or half a day, wrote a long-overdue letter or email to a family member, or made a difficult phone call. Be creative. Then give yourself a little party. Invite a special supporter, a family member or a child to join you. Or celebrate by yourself. Have a good time. The celebration can be as long or as short as you want it to be.

Things I could celebrate:

_____

_____

_____

How I could celebrate:

_____

_____

_____

These kinds of activities used consistently over time will help raise your self-esteem.

How We Develop Poor Self-esteem

Sometimes it helps to look back and discover where our poor self-esteem came from. Did it come from a very critical teacher? A jealous older sibling? A well-meaning aunt? Ads on television? Peers? Colleagues? You may want to explore the source of your negative self-esteem with a supporter. It helps to be with a trusted ally when working on difficult issues.

Who fed you this negative information about yourself?

_____

_____

_____

_____

Were these people really appropriate to be giving you this information? _____
No one has the right to be giving you negative information about yourself which would have a long term impact on your self-esteem.

As children, you don't have the ability to explore the validity of negative, inappropriate messages you receive about yourself. Most of us tend to believe anything that is said to us by our peers and adults.

For instance, my older brother, who teased and ridiculed me incessantly, was really not an appropriate source of information about the kind of person I am. However, being a child, I believed much of what he told me about myself.

Television advertisements that helped me define my feelings as a child and young adult also were a poor source of information about such an important subject. I thought I was supposed to look like people in the ads and do things the way they did.

Some of us have found it useful to give the negative source that fed us erroneous information about ourselves a name, such as klutz, stupid, jerk, dumbbell, bozo, good-for-nothing, worthless, etc. Close your eyes for a minute and find a name that most closely fits the source that is so critical of you.

What would that name be? _____
Does the name really fit? _____

If it doesn't, keep working on it until you find a name that really fits. It is much easier to get rid of a source that has a name, than one that just exists in some general way. It's a way of packaging the information and making it easier to deal with.

Once you have found a name that works, use it to help you let go of negative thoughts feelings about yourself. When they come up, say to yourself, "Oh, _____ made me feel that way." Then let it go. You may have to repeat this many times to really get rid of those negative thoughts and feelings.

Those of us who have gotten well, and stayed well, have only those people in our lives who affirm and validate us. If the people you associate with, family members, friends, or colleagues treat you badly, you can try to correct the situation by explaining the devastating effect that their comments and actions have on our self-esteem. They may not have realized the damage they were causing.

One person said her sister was very critical of her. She criticized the way she looked, the way she acted, the way she decorated her house, the way she raised her children, her career choice, every aspect of her being. It was a pattern that developed in childhood. When she told her sister how this made her feel, her sister was willing to work with her to correct the situation.

I am going to tell _____ how the way they treat me is making me feel about myself, and ask them not to do it.

If others persist in giving us inappropriate negative feedback, limit or avoid contact with these people as much as possible.

I went to a doctor for a time who was very critical and abrupt. When I left her office, I felt so bad about myself that it sometimes took me several days to get over it. Although her guidance on health care issues may have been right, it was negated by the terrible way she made me feel about myself. I changed doctors.

Another person said, "I used to think people could control me with their cruelty and manipulations. Only in the past few years have I decided to control my own emotions in a way where their comments and actions don't defeat me. I immediately rattle off all my good points when others try to make me feel small. I am constantly telling myself that I have unique good qualities that nobody else has. I use these affirmations at work, when there is tension. I use them when I am sure someone isn't giving me credit for what I do."

I recently received negative feedback from an angry family member. In the past, such input would have devastated me. Now, while I am very sad that this person feels this way, my own sense of myself and who I am is so strong that this episode did not affect my self-esteem.

I am going to avoid contact with _____ because it is so damaging to my self-esteem.

Is there anyone in your life right now who is feeding you negative, inappropriate messages about yourself?

_____
_____
_____

How does it make you feel?

_____
_____
_____

What are you going to do about it?

_____
_____
_____

Examples of circumstances that can contribute to low self-esteem:

- loss of jobs and career opportunities
- unstable or failed relationships
- estrangement from or poor relationships with family members
- the inability to be self supporting
- the inability to complete educational programs and meet educational goals
- a loss of credibility in the community
- embarrassment, shame and guilt from unusual behavior

What circumstances of your life have lowered your self-esteem and self-confidence?

_____

_____

_____

_____

How valid were these circumstances as determinants of your worth?

_____

_____

_____

_____

The best antidote to being affected by negative input is to have a clear picture of yourself and who you are, being able to judge for yourself whether or not there is any validity to what another person is saying, or what a circumstance seems to be telling you about yourself.

I have a positive statement of my own worth, that I have internalized, which enhances my life and helps me deal with difficult situations. It has been my savior when I have feelings of low self-esteem.

My positive statement of my worth.

I, Mary Ellen, am an amazing, unique, valuable and wonderful person. Others like me because I am friendly, warm and compassionate. I like people and have a strong empathy for others. I always do the best I can and am competent and responsible. I am honest and trustworthy. I have a good education, have successfully raised five wonderful children, and have helped many people improve their lives.

Write a statement of your own positive worth. What are you really like? What kind of a person are you? What wonderful things have you accomplished? Do it as if you were doing it for someone else. **No negatives allowed.** You will notice that I have left lots of space. Fill it up.

_____

_____

_____

_____

_____

_____

_____

Make several copies of this statement. Keep them in convenient places like on your bedside table, in your pocket, purse, or glove compartment, taped to the mirror in the bathroom, or stuck to the refrigerator door.

Read it over and over to yourself. Memorize it. Then, whenever you start thinking negative thoughts about yourself, repeat it, silently if you are with others, or aloud if you are alone. As you feel better about yourself, you may realize that you can update your statement of your own worth to make it even more positive.

Spend time with people who affirm and validate you.

I am going to spend time with the following people who affirm and validate me:

_____

_____

_____

_____

_____

Many of us have spent years of hard work learning how to change our focus away from negative thoughts about ourselves and onto thoughts and activities that are positive.

Tim Field, a mental health activist, says:

> Dealing with the thought problems is different. I find my thoughts are plenty 'disordered' when I am depressed. What happens to me is that negative thoughts and useless worries intrude upon my normal thinking. Suddenly a thought such as 'You're a bad person' or 'Why don't you kill yourself?' or 'How are you going to afford to get your car fixed?' will superimpose itself on whatever I was thinking about, like a tape-loop from hell, an evil spirit whispering in

my ear. I keep track of how often this happens as a measure of how depressed I am. On a 'normal' day the intrusions may occur just four or five times or maybe not at all. If they begin to happen 50 times an hour or more, I find myself quite impaired. As the intrusion escalates, so do the obsessive worries. I worry about everything, and can't stop it.

I think contending with the intrusions and worries are the taxing elements that deplete my usual energy. Normal decisions that I make 100 times a day seem to become vastly complicated and overwhelming and therefore too tiring and scary and more than I can handle at the moment. One way I deal with this is to make every effort to put off decisions or actions that seem too overwhelming. If something can't be put off, I ask someone in my support team for advice and/or help if I don't feel up to it or I'm not sure what to do.

One woman said, "Some nights I pull an 'all-nighter'. That means I don't sleep. When I have been awake for 36 plus hours I find I start thinking negatively. So I change my thoughts by inserting something positive. It really works. Or I can go to sleep and wake up talking very positively." She says, "I try to find 'the good' in everything that happens. I don't carry grudges. 'I don't know if I can do this?' becomes 'Yes, I can do this'. If I think I can, I will do it. Think that you can do it and you will do it."

I talked to a woman who used to tell herself, "I'm no good." She replaces that thought by making a list of her good points. When she is taking on too much at one time, and feeding herself negative input because she doesn't get it all done, she counters it by doing a little of something each day. The thought "I have no time to do anything I want" is opposed by actually taking time out each day to do something she enjoys, such as crafts, reading, or watching television.

A woman who has been well for ten years has taught herself, "I am OK, everything is not my fault," and "I don't have to please everyone."

One woman remarked, "I work on this daily. I try to be aware of negative thought patterns and 'reverse' them by reframing the thoughts around the situation. My therapist and various readings have assisted me in this process."

When speaking about how she encourages herself, a woman said, "I always have difficulty when I am sliding into a depressed phase because I think the bottom may fall out, I will lose control and need to hospitalized and worry that would ruin all the growth I have made professionally. I then tell myself I have not been hospitalized since 1985. I have felt this way before and have been able to make it through. I can talk with my therapist and doctor."

Here are some affirmations shared by a woman who uses them especially on days when she is feeling low, worn out with lots of worry ("I seem to be saying affirmations while just walking or driving my car."):

I am a good person.

I am worth loving.

I am intelligent.

I am confident.

I enjoy my new life.

There is hope in faith and strength.

I must continue to go forth.

"When I find feelings that are difficult to deal with, I stop and say the affirmation in my head, and it becomes easier to let go of that feeling."

Other examples of negative thoughts that study participants have changed to positive ones include:

Negative Thought	Positive Thought
I can't control any of my depressed feelings.	I control my depressed feelings.
I am stupid.	I am smart.
I'm not OK.	I am OK.
I've had it. I'm going to give up.	I'm going to stay the course.
This situation is going to last forever.	This situation will improve.
I can't handle it.	I can handle it.
I am incompetent.	I am competent.
I am a bad person.	I am a good person.
I can't do anything.	I can do anything I want to do.
I am weak and ineffective.	I am a strong and powerful person.
My personality stinks.	I have a fantastic personality.

Use the following space to write down your negative thoughts and their positive counterparts.

Negative Thought	Positive Thought
_____	_____
_____	_____
_____	_____
_____	_____
_____	_____
_____	_____
_____	_____
_____	_____

Techniques that reinforce positive thoughts and increase self-esteem:

Thought Stopping - Every time the negative perception comes up, say to it, in a firm voice (in your mind if you are with others) "shut up," "stop," "be quiet," "go away"- whatever works for you.

Affirmations - Write positive statements on a piece of paper. Carry it with you. Repeat it them over and over to yourself, when you are waiting at a traffic light, waiting for an appointment, before you go to bed at night, as many times as you can.

Meditation - Relax your body using progressive relaxation techniques. Then repeat the positive thought while you are in this relaxed state.

Visualization - Relax your body using progressive relaxation techniques. Then picture yourself feeling the way your positive thought would make you feel while saying it to yourself.

Journaling - Use your journal as a place to write about the process of changing negative thoughts to positive.

Signs - Make signs, to post around your home, that have positive statements that you have developed. Read them several times when you see them.

Exchange Listening - Get together with a friend you trust and repeat positive thoughts about yourself over and over. Then give them a chance to do the same.

Counseling - Regular meetings with a counselor you trust can help raise your self-esteem and self-confidence. Share with the counselor your lists of negative perceptions and positive affirmations.

Which of these techniques are you going to try?

_____

_____

_____

_____

You may find that when you are repeating positive thoughts about yourself, it brings up some emotion, usually crying. Expressing the emotion helps to reinforce the positive thoughts.

Refer to the chapters "Exchange Listening," "Focusing," "Counseling" and "Trauma" for more ideas for enhancing your self-esteem by changing negative thoughts to positive ones.

Develop a sense of compassion for yourself. Love yourself and treat yourself that way. You are a wonderful, unique person. Be gentle and forgiving with yourself.

Lifestyle Issues

Careers and Work

It has taken a long time to get to this place where I really feel like the work I am doing is the work I am supposed to be doing.

People who deal with mental health challenges have successfully worked at many different jobs and in many different fields. The careers are as varied as the people themselves. This includes being teachers, psychologists, counselors, health care caseworkers, accountants, dietitians, sales people, doctors, nurses, social workers, custodians, surveyors, tool and die makers, electricians, plumbers, carpenters, secretaries, child care workers, journalists, truck drivers, sales people, computer operators and programmers, florists – the list goes on and on. The message is clear – people with mental health challenges can usually do anything with their lives that they want to. They may be successfully self-employed or work for a small firm, organization, or large corporation.

You may have chosen not to work at a career but to live an active, full, and rewarding life that may include advocacy, volunteering, raising a family, caring for elderly parents or relatives with disabilities, or pursuing an interest or talent. For instance, a person I interviewed said:

"I went ahead and filled out your questionnaire even though I have not been working for a year and a half. I did this because I feel the measure of someone's mental health is not holding a job. I feel I am better off now than if I had been working. I am not depressed. I am taking care of my daily affairs. I manage my income from social security disability. Being on social security is not a dreadful thing, it's a fact of life."

If you don't have to work and that is your preference, that's great. Many people prefer to have a career and find that a career improves the quality of their lives and raises their self-esteem. You can make your own decision about this.

Tim Field of Seattle, Washington, says:

"Because of the class structure in the United States, it is nearly essential for everyone to be on a 'career path' if they wish to be perceived as 'one of us' and not as some kind of a failure or 'weirdo'. This is really most unfortunate. Having a 'successful career' or 'good job' is the crux of self-esteem for most people.

My experience has induced me to simply reject the career path model with its heavy baggage of failure and guilt.

"I accept responsibility at work if I feel I am up to it and want to, but I don't allow myself to get into a position where a large project or an entire department is dependent on me. It has worked better for me to find other sources of reward than career advancement, which by nature requires accepting more and more responsibilities, only to have them taken away when I get depressed. This means a different approach to life goals, but I think it's only prudent. Why beat your head against the wall trying to advance to the 'top' at some silly job only to be batted down and humiliated every time you get depressed? There are more important things than a good job, and I focus on these as sources for positive strokes for my self-esteem.

"The effects of depression have led me to abandon the upwardly mobile 'career path' model and to direct my efforts and sources of self-esteem elsewhere. Perhaps this would have happened anyway. What matters most is finding something that *works*, that is rewarding regardless of my opinion of options I no longer have."

Before mental health challenges overtook my life, I had several careers. My first was as a homemaker, raising five children and caring for a large home. As the children needed less of my time, I went back to college to complete the final two years toward my bachelor's degree in special education. For a number of years, I was a special education teacher and directed a small private school for students with special needs. In the early 1980s, I decided a career change was in order. I wanted to focus my energies on a deep personal passion – environmental issues. I went back to school for a Master of Science in Resource Management and Administration. While in graduate school, and for several years thereafter, I worked as a development director in the very stressful position of raising money for several national environmental organizations.

When I was in my mid-forties, the mental health issues that I had successfully controlled with medications overpowered me and, for a time, took control of my life. I reluctantly gave up my career because I was no longer able to keep up with the performance requirements. I supported myself through Social Security and other entitlement programs.

My psychiatrist referred me to vocational rehabilitation services to find work that I could manage. My work with vocational rehabilitation eased me into a new career, well-suited to my interests, talents and abilities, where I am my own boss, free to do whatever is necessary to keep myself stable. This new career as a mental health educator has given me a sense of accomplishment, satisfaction and security.

When I first went to vocational rehabilitation, I had no idea what I wanted to do or how I wanted to proceed. Mental health education was not my original career goal. Through a long process that included a structured evaluation of my education, experience, interests, and talents, along with long term vocational counseling, I discovered my interest in finding out how people with issues like mine manage their lives, and in sharing that information with others.

My first vocational goal was to be a researcher and technical writer. I developed the skills necessary for such a career through studying people who live with mental health issues, compiling the collected data and writing a technical book on the results of my study. I met these goals with ongoing support and assistance from vocational rehabilitation and the financial assistance of a Social Security Plan to Achieve Self-Support (PASS). The PASS gave me the funds needed to purchase a computer, develop research materials, and gather data.

As a result of interest in my research, I gave several presentations that were very successful. I also found interest in a workbook based on my findings. I set up a new goal for myself. That was to become a public speaker and author. I got another PASS to help me meet these new goals. My new career has taken me to new levels of personal and financial achievement, satisfaction, and independence.

In making decisions about work and career, consider that many people with mental health issues use the skills they have learned in dealing with these disorders to develop careers in mental health education, support, counseling , peer counseling, advocacy and administration. Our life experience makes us especially effective in these roles. For instance, David Hilton, the former Director of the Office of Consumer Affairs used the strengths he had learned in dealing with years of mental health issues to effectively establish programs in New Hampshire for others with similar challenges.

Career Assessment

Is your current work or career satisfactory? _____
Does your work enhance your wellness?_____
Would you like to pursue a different career, one that matches your special needs, interests and abilities? _____
If you feel you need to pursue a career, or a different career, at this time, give careful attention to the following considerations. Then, using the exercise provided, proceed with planning how to make this change.

Scheduling While most people with mental health challenges are able to work and do a good job, they often find that their peak performance times do not coincide with those of other workers, or with the times an employer would prefer they work. Their performance improved when work was task related rather than time related. For instance, rather than work an eight hour day from 9-5 each day, having an assignment or project to complete with broader timelines fit their work style. This is difficult in many work settings. However, other people said they work better with a structured schedule.

___ I work best when time schedules are flexible.

___ I perform at my optimum when my schedule is structured.

People with mental health issues have found that it is best to avoid changing shifts, for example working from 7-3 for two weeks, 3 to 11 for two weeks, and 11-7 for two weeks. They also don't do well with the 11-7 shift.

Low Stress Those of us with mental health issues do not perform well in pressured work environments. In the work situation I was in when my mental health issues became overwhelming, I was under a lot of pressure. The organization was operating, as it had been for a long time, with income that was barely meeting its expenses. Employees were in fear of being laid off. The success of key programs was dependent on limited accessible funds. I was a fundraiser. Intense pressure was my daily companion. It was very hard for me to leave my work behind and enjoy other parts of my life. I burned out very quickly.

____ I need a low stress position or career.
Why?

_____
_____
_____
_____

Private Space The availability of private space, where one can shut the door, be quiet and alone is important to many people. They do not want a job where they are isolated, but they want private space to be available on an as needed basis. For instance, a woman who has been a guidance counselor for over 20 years, says she has never taken off more than six weeks. After two months off in the summer, she is ready to start school in the Fall. She makes her job manageable by having her own office, with a door she can close and shut out the world, no classroom lesson plans, and no papers to correct at home.

I have my office at home. It gives me quiet time to work. When I want people around, I check in with my spouse, find a friend to go for a walk, or go into town to do errands. People are as close as my phone. My workshops and presentations also give me needed contact with others. My office is separated from the rest of the house. I can close the door and put my work behind me when I need space from it.

_____ I need accessibility to private space in my work place.

Understanding Employers Some people share their mental health history with their employer. Others, hoping that that it will not become an issue, have chosen not to divulge that information. In either event, understanding employers may be difficult to find, but they are definitely an asset.

Tim Field shares his recent work experience:

"For the last few years I have been completely up-front about my mental health with my employer. I may not always volunteer everything, but I feel that I have nothing to hide (because there is nothing to be ashamed of). Everybody has problems, and if I have to be Mr. Clean to work for them, it's not the kind of place where I want to work anyway."

"In terms of how I handle down-time from the job, I have made an agreement with the owner of the company that if I'm not up to it, I can be absent. I can take vacation or sick leave until they are used up, and then go on leave without pay. This approach requires being frank and up-front about your situation and having an employer who values the big picture."

If you are being hired for your abilities, and accommodations for your mental health issues are not necessary, then you don't have to tell your employer in advance. However, if you were in a situation where accommodations would be necessary, then the employer should be notified. By making a careful job choice, accommodations may not be necessary.

The Americans with Disabilities Act (ADA) guarantees equal opportunity to people with disabilities in the areas of employment, state and local government services, public accommodations and telecomunications. If you feel your mental health issues are affecting your work situation or your ability to be employed, contact:

National Rehabilitation Information Center
ABLEDATA Database of Assistive Technology
8201 Corporate Dr., Suite 600
Landover, MD 20785
800/346-2742 or 301/459-5900

They have a Resource Guide which contains information on a variety of ADA materials including guides, manuals, publications, training programs, and technical assistance programs.

Those employers who are willing to take the risk and hire a person with a history of mental health issues will find that, while the person may have times when they are not up to par, or when time off is needed to address these issues, when they are able to work, they make up for the "down-time" in increased productivity.

_____ I choose to tell my employer or prospective employer about my mental health issues.
When (before or after I am hired?) _____
Why?

_____
_____
_____
_____

_____ I will not share information with my employer about my mental health issues.
Why not?

_____
_____
_____

Creativity People who experience mental health issues are among the brightest and most creative people in our society. Therefore, they need creative jobs that take advantage of their superior abilities. They do not do well in repetitious, controlled work circumstances.

_____ Creativity in my career is very important to me.

That means:

_____
_____
_____

Creative Job Development Many people, including me, have found that creative job development that may mean self-employment. It may be the best way to meet needs for flexible scheduling, low stress, private space and creativity in their career.

I developed, over several years, a successful career as a mental health educator, lecturing, presenting workshops, and developing educational resources. When I need a break, I can take one. If I feel like working late into the night, that's all right too. I schedule my work to meet my personal needs. My new career, directed by me, makes good use of my abilities and creativity.

A woman I interviewed developed a career raising exotic birds after her job as a chef ended. She feels her work with birds plays an important role in her wellness. Their care keeps her going. Initiative was the key! She developed the new career on her own. She reports that a vocational rehabilitation program was somewhat helpful. She said she had a hard time convincing them that she needed to work on her own. She says, "I think they would have been more helpful if I wanted a traditional career, but they are supporting my endeavors." She said it's important to let vocational counselors know what you really want and that you want their support in reaching your goal.

_____ Creative job development sounds as if it is the answer for me.

Share your dream of a new career (this dream may change while you are bringing it to reality).

_____

_____

_____

_____

What are the interests, talents and abilities you want to use in your career? _____

_____

_____

_____

_____

_____

_____

In what ways will this career meet your scheduling, low stress, understanding employers and creativity requirements?

_____

_____

Which criteria will be difficult to meet? _____

_____

_____

_____

Using your creative problem-solving abilities, describe how you can effectively deal with the criteria that are more difficult to meet? _____

_____

_____

_____

_____

What is the first step you need to take to begin the process of creative job development? (You may want to consider the rest of this chapter before answering this question.)

_____

_____

_____

_____

List intermediate goals such as education, training or equipment purchases necessary to your career choice.

_____

_____

_____

_____

_____

_____

HELP Take advantage of the following resources to find a job that is right for you or to assist and support you in creating a career for yourself.

Vocational Rehabilitation The federal government, in cooperation with state governments, has set up a nationwide system of vocational rehabilitation services. Vocational Rehabilitation services provide various kinds of vocational assistance and support to people with disabilities. If you have lost your job because of mental health difficulties, your job is not appropriate to your special needs. Contact your local or state office of Vocational Rehabilitation. To receive services, you may need to present medical documents or a statement from your physician to verify your condition.

Don't wait until you know exactly what you want to do. If careers are an issue for you, establish your connection with Vocational Rehabilitation services right away. They have a wide variety of resources available to guide and assist in all phases of your career development and can help you develop a step-by-step approach to achieving your goals.

____I have been in touch with vocational rehabilitation services.

Assistance provided:

_____

_____

_____

____ I am going to contact vocational rehabilitation services.

I am going to ask them to help me:

_____

_____

_____

Employment and Training Services States are federally mandated to provide individuals with free employment and training services, such as aptitude testing, job screening, job referrals, placements and vocational counseling. These offices have comprehensive listings of area employment opportunities.

____ I am going to contact Employment and Training Services.

Services I plan to explore or request:

_____

_____

_____

Job Partnership Training (JPT) Job Partnership Training is another federally mandated program. In some states it is administered by Employment and Training Services while in other states it is administered by private agencies. JPT provides on-the-job placement services, job training and education, and resources such as equipment and licensing fees needed to get into the job force. JPT is dependent on a yearly funding cycle.

____ I am going to contact the Job Partnership Training Program in my area.

I am going to request the following assistance:

_____

_____

_____

SCORE SCORE is an acronym for Service Corps of Retired Executives. This is a program of volunteer retired executives, who give free assistance to people who are starting businesses. Depending on their experience, they will help develop business plans, set up bookkeeping systems, fill out loan applications, develop marketing plans and strategies, etc.

_____ I am going to contact SCORE for assistance.

I am going to request the following assistance:

_____

_____

_____

Small Business Development Centers Each state has federal- and state-funded Small Business Centers which provide in-depth counseling assistance at no cost to people starting new businesses or to existing firms. Their services include a comprehensive resource referral library. They sponsor workshops on a variety of business related topics. Phone 1-800-8-ASK-SBA (SMALL BUSINESS ADMINISTRATION) for more information.

Office of Economic Development Many larger towns and regions have Offices of Economic Development that provide a range of services to businesses. Check the phone book to find such offices in your area.

Libraries and the Internet Libraries are an excellent source of information to use in the job development process. They are a great way to find educational facilities and programs, career ideas, organizations, corporations, how-to references, etc. In addition, there are many sites on the internet that can help you with whatever you are trying to do. Be patient and keep looking. Eventually, you will find what it is that you want to know.

_____ I am going to the library.

___ I am going to do an internet search.

I am going to look up information on:

_____

_____

_____

PASS Plans PASS is the acronym for Social Security Plans to Achieve Self-Support. If you have a work history and receive Social Security Disability Insurance, you may be eligible for funds that would allow you to meet vocational goals in anticipation of resuming employment, or starting your own business. PASS Plans will pay for almost anything that will help you reach your work goal, up to the amount of your current benefit. This includes:

- supplies to start a business
- tuition, fees, books and supplies needed for school or training
- supported-employment services
- attendant or child care expenses
- equipment and tools to do the job
- transportation to and from work
- uniforms, special clothing, and safety equipment

You can get assistance in setting up such a plan from a vocational rehabilitation counselor, an employer or the Social Security office. If you are interested in such a plan, call your Social Security office or research PASS on-line.

_____ I am going to find out more about Social Security PASS Plans.
_____ A Social Security PASS Plan sounds as if it would work for me. I am going to develop and submit a PASS Plan with help and support from _____ .

Check with your Office of Vocational Rehabilitation and Employment and Training Services for information on other programs with services that may be useful.

Education and Training You may discover that, to meet your career goal, you need additional training or education. While traditional educational programs may be well suited to your needs, you may want to explore the possibility of enrollment in an alternative program that is designed for students with special needs. Vocational rehabilitation and employment and training services will have information on these programs.

I got my Master's in Resource Management and Administration in a program that met my scheduling needs, with classes that met evenings and weekends. I was able to get credit for documented life experience. My Master's in counseling psychology program was self-directed. I developed a comprehensive plan for studies, writings, projects, and presentations to meet program requirements. I worked on my own with support and advice from faculty advisers. Each semester I attended one all-day seminar. I got my doctorate in a similar self-directed program.

Community colleges and adult education programs offer a wide variety of education and training options.

Many schools have an Office of Disability Support Services (ODSS). Talk to them about your specific issues. You may need "documentation" (such as a medical report) of your disability to present to the ODSS. It is only after you come forward with such documentation that the ODSS can provide you with accommodative services. **However, your treatment history is confidential and you do not need to disclose it unless you choose to do so.**

It may be helpful to take a reduced number of classes the first several semesters until you get acclimated to the new environment and lifestyle.

Become familiar with the resources on your campus. There may be a learning center, or its equivalent, that will assist you in sharpening your study skills and provide tutoring services. Some counseling centers provide support groups for students returning to campus after an absence.

Before you return to school, contact the college's financial aid officer for information on financial awards. This assistance could help you to finance your education. If disability prevents repayment of student loans, contact the lender immediately and request a medical deferment. Note that granting deferment of your payments is not automatic. You must continue to make payments until you are notified that the deferment has been processed and approved. If you do not, you may be in default. Once your loan is in default, it can be difficult to change that status.

If you have to leave school, withdraw officially so that you do not fail your classes by default. In some cases you may be able to have the designation "Incomplete" recorded, thereby earning the right to complete the requirements later.

Lifestyle Issues

Developing A Lifestyle that Enhances Wellness

It's the hardest thing for me, keeping my life in control
and doing for myself the things that I know are best for me.

You may find that you have a difficult time keeping your life in balance. You may have identified key lifestyle factors that affect the way you feel. In addition, you may have identified activities and strategies that make you feel even better. By paying close attention to all these factors, like many others, you may have developed a lifestyle that enhances your wellness and contributes to the enjoyment of your life. In this chapter, we will review things that others have found useful to them in their wellness and recovery. You will note that many of them fit very well in the Wellness Toolbox described in the first section of this book.

Light

Many people fear the onset of winter because, as the days shorten, they feel more and more and more "depressed." Do you experience any of the following signs of insufficient light in the winter months, as the days get shorter and winter approaches?

_____ drop in energy level
_____ difficulty getting out of bed in the morning
_____ impatient with self and others
_____ craving sweets and high carbohydrate foods
_____ creativity decreases
_____ difficulty concentrating and focusing
_____ diminished sex drive
_____ difficulty getting motivated
_____ decrease in productivity

If so, the culprit may be Seasonal Affective Disorder, more commonly known as SAD.
You may notice the same effect on cloudy days. You may feel even worse after several cloudy days.

_____ I notice that I feel "low" on cloudy days or after several cloudy days.

Researchers have found that consistent daily exposure to bright light through the eyes reduces, or eliminates, these feelings for many people with SAD. A simple program that increases the natural light or bright light through the eyes often helps people feel better.

If you think you may have SAD, discuss it with your physician. While many people have successfully treated themselves, a health care provider with expertise in the field of light therapy will:

- make sure light therapy is appropriate and there are no other medical conditions which need treatment
- work with you to develop a treatment strategy that fits your schedule and lifestyle
- assist with monitoring
- provide additional ideas, and alternative or supplemental treatment options
- give encouragement, and support

If you are taking certain photosensitizing medications, or have a condition which causes you to have sun sensitive skin, such as lupus, a health care provider is essential to developing the treatment process.

_____ I am going to discuss light therapy with health care provider. If so, who and why?

_____

_____

If seeing a health care provider about this issue is not an option for you, check out one of the many books on this issue and do an internet search for even more information.

___ Seeing a health care provider about SAD is not an option for me. Therefore, I am going to do the following to address this issue:

_____

_____

_____

_____

In any case, increasing the light through their eyes through outdoor activity helps many people. Never look directly at sun. The amount of light you get outside is enhanced by reflection off snow, and reduced by reflection off dark objects, such as buildings and trees.

Keeping your living space well lit also helps. Windows should be uncovered during the daylight hours to let sunlight in. If you work inside, work as close to a window as possible.

Tanning booths are not recommended for light therapy.

Some people report SAD-like feelings in the summer. However, people with summer depressions tend to be more agitated, while those of us who have winter depressions are more sedated. This may be a result of temperature sensitivity. Some people have relieved these feelings by spending time in an air- conditioned space. You may want to give that a try. Try it for several days to see if it helps. Adjust the length of exposure to see if that makes a difference.

_____ I notice that I feel "low" in the summer months.
_____ I will spend time in an air-conditioned room to see if it helps me feel better.

Time spent:_____

How I felt before I spent time in an air-conditioned room.

_____

_____

How I felt after spending time in an air-conditioned room.

_____

_____

As a result of my findings I am going to:

_____

_____

_____ I will discuss these signs and their possible relationship to temperature with my health care provider for additional suggestions.

Exercise

People who have gotten well, and stayed well, exercise regularly. In addition to the numerous physiological benefits of exercise, Dr. Edmund Bourne in *The Anxiety and Phobia Workbook* reports the following psychological benefits:

- increased feeling of well-being
- reduced dependence on alcohol and drugs
- reduced insomnia
- improved concentration and memory
- alleviation of depression symptoms
- greater control over feelings of anxiety
- increased self-esteem

Any kind of exercise is acceptable. Walking, swimming, skating, skiing, dancing – even outdoor chores such as gardening, and raking. You can do the same kind of exercise every day, or vary it according to the weather, what you feel like, and other things you need to get done. Yesterday, I spent part of my exercise time shoveling snow, and breaking up ice on my driveway. This makes exercise more interesting for some of us. You don't have to join an expensive health club (although it is a wonderful treat if you can afford it). The exercise does not have to be strenuous. Even a stroll helps.

What kinds of exercise do you enjoy?

_____

_____

_____

Walking is the easiest, most convenient and best exercise. It works well for most people because:

- No special equipment is necessary except a good pair of walking shoes.

- It doesn't cost anything.

- It is non-competitive, so old feelings of not being as good as others don't come up.

- You can walk any time, anywhere that is safe. Many people walk on the track at a local high school after school hours. I find that walking on one of the rural walking trails or abandoned roads in our area has the added benefit of communion with nature.

- You can walk in whatever you happen to be wearing.

- You don't have to change your clothes or take a shower after walking.

- It is very unlikely that you will incur the type of overuse injuries that occur with other types of exercise.

You may have had difficulty beginning, or sticking to, an exercise program. You may feel that you don't have time, that it interferes with other responsibilities, and that you won't enjoy it. Solve this problem by looking at your exercise time as fun, not as work. Consider it play-time. You need play to feel well. Remember the old adage, "All work and no play makes Jack a dull boy." Consider combining exercise with other strategies you use to maintain your stability.

For instance:

- When exercising outdoors, your exposure to light is increased.

- When exercising indoors you can do it in front of a light box.

- It's a good time to practice focusing on positive thoughts.

- You can connect with peers, family members and supporters by asking them to join you on a walk.

- You can exchange listen while walking.

What other ways can you combine exercise with other strategies you use to maintain your stability?

_____

_____

_____

I find it helps me to stick to my exercise program if I reward myself (my kids call it bribing) at regular intervals. I may put aside a dollar each time I exercise, toward an article of clothing, a CD, or some other treat. After a week of successful exercise, I may treat myself to a healthy lunch out with a special friend. After exercising becomes part of your routine, you won't need to reward yourself, as you will find that the exercise itself is ample reward.

To help me stick to my exercise plan, I will:

_____

_____

_____

Scheduling exercise at the same time each day provides structure and helps to insure continuation of an exercise program.

I will exercise (time of day) _____ , (days a week)_____ , for (length of time) _____ .

If you have not exercised regularly, begin gradually, starting with a few minutes of exercise and working up to 20 minutes a day or 30 to 45 minutes three to five times a week.

If you start out too fast, you may find that the resulting aches and pains are discouraging and may keep you from continuing. A warm bath after you exercise the first few times also helps to relieve aches and pains.

Many of us have found it difficult to exercise in the winter and in bad weather. You can solve that problem by purchasing a piece of exercise equipment, such as an exercise bicycle or rowing machine. You can often find these at very low prices in the bargain sections of the newspaper (being sold by people who had good intentions, but never followed through). Other people exercise by walking up and down stairs. I often put on some good music and dance.

See your physician before starting an exercise program if you have a health condition which may be affected.

_____ I am going to start exercising today. I am going to (type of exercise) _____ for (how long) _____.

Diet

What you eat affects the way you feel. Diet plays a significant role in working toward wellness and recovery. There are numerous diet guidelines available and lots of controversy over the best diet. Diet is a personal thing and over time, watching what you eat and how you feel after you eat it, you will discover what works best for you. There are many excellent books and lots of resources on the internet that can give you guidance. If you can see a qualified nutritionist, that is even better.

Issues that could affect your diet choices might include blood sugar control, weight gain or loss, allergies, cultural customs, and personal finances. I recently talked with a friend who had been treated with psychiatric medications for many years and was told that she was incurably mentally ill and would need to take medications for the rest of her life. Tests by an alternative care provider showed that she had celiac disease, an allergy to products that contain gluten (most grains). With the change of diet, her "mental illness" disappeared.

These days, most people agree that vegetables are good, and the more vegetables you include in your diet (as many as seven servings a day), the better. That is where the agreement stops. Some diets say eat lots of grains, some say moderate amounts of grains, and some say no grains at all. There are similar controversies over how much protein you need, how much fat you should have in your diet, and the value of dairy products. You will need to sort all of this out for yourself, figuring out what works best for you.

However, many people report that refined sugar, foods that are high in saturated fat, high in calories, have low food value (junk food), and/or processed foods that contain lots of additives, alcohol, and caffeine can make you feel worse and impede their recovery.

Through carefully watching your diet and eliminating foods that have a negative affect on how you feel, you can improve your health.

What foods have you noticed make you feel badly?

_____

_____

_____

_____

I have often found it difficult to stick to a good diet that I know promotes my wellness. When I am very busy, trying to meet a deadline, or preparing for a trip, I put my good eating habits on the back burner. I don't take the time to go grocery shopping, or to prepare good food for myself. When I am traveling, I find it very difficult, and in some cases impossible, to find well prepared, reasonably priced, healthy food. I sometimes end up dealing with my hunger by snacking on junk foods. I always pay with a general feeling of malaise and development of acute gastrointestinal symptoms.

I know what I need to do for myself. Perhaps some of these ideas will be helpful to you. I need to:

    1. Make regular shopping trips a high priority, so that I have healthy foods on hand.

    2. Take the time to cook good foods for myself.

    3. Keep a supply of easy to fix healthy foods on hand to prepare when I am busy.

    4. Identify several local restaurants where I can go for a healthy meal.

    5. Pack a supply of healthy snacks in my carry-on luggage for use when I am traveling.

    6. Let hosts know of my food needs and ask them to help me locate restaurants in the area which would meet my dietary needs.

What problems do you have sticking with a healthy diet?

_____

_____

_____

_____

_____

How could you solve these problems?

_____

_____

_____

_____

_____

If you are temporarily house-bound, or your schedule is hectic, ask a supporter to pick up groceries for you when they pick up their own. You can return the favor when you are able. If getting out is always difficult for you, contact a home health aid service in your area for grocery delivery service. In some areas, nutritious meals can be delivered to your home.

You may have used, or are using, various amino acid and vitamin regimens to improve your general health and your mental health. If possible, develop your supplement program in consultation with knowledgeable health care providers including nutritionists and naturopathic physicians. In addition, there are many good books on using supplements, and lots of information on the internet. If you are taking prescription medications, tell your physician about your use of supplements and ask him or her to make sure the ones you are using are safe to use with your medication. I have changed to a medical doctor who also has a strong background in using supplements to achieve good health.

_____ I am going to explore the use of dietary supplements.

_____ I am going to consult with the following health care providers regarding the use of supplements.

_____

_____

_____ I am committed to improving my diet.

Sleep Getting a good night's sleep is important to overall wellness and recovery. However, many people report that they have difficulties with insomnia. Others report that when they are feeling badly, they sometimes sleep all the time. Overall, people report that lack of sleep, or too much sleep makes them feel worse and hinders their wellness.

Healthy habits for getting a good night's sleep:

- Go to bed at the same time every night and get up at the same time every morning.
- Avoid "sleeping in."
- Have regular, daytime work hours, avoiding shift and overnight work.
- Get up at the usual hour, even you haven't slept well.
- Avoid or limit your caffeine intake.
- Give up smoking (nicotine is a stimulant and can keep you awake).
- Avoid the use of alcohol. (While it may help you fall asleep, it will disturb your sleep later and may cause you to awaken early.)
- Eat on a regular schedule and avoid a heavy meal prior to going to bed.
- Avoid rigid weight loss plans that will cause you to wake up hungry during the night.
- Distribute your calorie intake throughout the day.
- Have an adequate calcium intake. (A calcium supplement often helps people sleep.)
- Exercise daily.
- Avoid exercising, and strenuous or invigorating activity, before going to bed.
- Have a daily routine so your body knows when it is time to go to sleep.
- Avoid taking long naps during the day.
- Have a pre-bedtime ritual that you follow that tells your body its time to go to bed, such as washing up, getting into night clothes, reading a chapter from a book.
- Keep your bedroom temperature between 65 and 70 degrees Farenheit.
- Make sure your sleeping space is not too noisy, light or busy.

What health habits do you need to improve to insure proper sleep?

_____

_____

_____

_____

Activities that may help you sleep well

- Use progressive relaxation exercises (those where you tense and relax muscles) to put yourself to sleep. I do this often. I repeat the exercise if I wake up during the night. I have an IPod beside my bed with a choice of relaxation exercises on it to use when I am having a hard time getting to sleep.

- Play soothing music that shuts off automatically after a set amount of time.

- Focus your attention on your breathing when you are trying to get to sleep and repeat the words "in"and "out" silently as you breathe.

- Use your imaging skills to put yourself to sleep. Consider:
    1. Painting a landscape in your mind.
    2. Imagining numbers, starting with one, embellished with various decorations. When you have finished with each number, mentally erase it and go on to the next.
    3. Visualizing yourself walking slowly on a sandy beach on a warm spring day. The gulls are flying overhead. You can hear the waves breaking on the shore. You lay down on the sand and feel the warm sun relaxing you.
    4. You can think of many more imagery exercises that will relax you and promote sleep. You can also use guided imagery CDs.

- Focus your attention on feelings of warmth and heaviness. Work through your body progressively, suggesting to each part that it feels heavy and warm.

- Read a non-stimulating book before going to bed.

- Write in your journal about anything and everything until you feel too tired to write anymore. I keep a journal by my bed. If I wake up during the night and can't get back to sleep because I have too much on my mind, I write it all down and then go back to sleep.

- A turkey sandwich and a glass of milk before bedtime makes many people feel drowsy.

- Health food stores have safe, natural preparations that many people find useful in relieving insomnia. Get recommendations from a naturopathic physician or nutritionist.

What strategies have you successfully used to insure a good nights sleep?

_____
_____
_____
_____

What are you going to use to help you get a goodnight's sleep?

_____
_____
_____
_____

Only use medications for temporary relief of sleep problems, and then under the guidancee of your physician. Many sleep medications are addictive. There is no medication that can cure insomnia. The underlying cause must be discovered and addressed. If you are having persistent sleep problems, see your physician to develop a treatment plan.

Living Space

A comfortable living space is important to achieving long term wellness.

I used to live in a dark, cold cabin in the middle of nowhere. While I was having mental health challenges, I still had to maintain a cabin with no drinking water, no indoor plumbing, no insulation, no light, and a wood stove that ate nine cords of wood a year. I had to stack those nine cords, and couldn't leave the cabin for more than 4 hours at a time. The snow was always so deep and took forever to melt due to its location. I couldn't figure out why I wasn't getting any better. When I finally moved, it was hard and expensive, but worth it.

The following factors need to be explored when considering appropriate living space.

Do you look forward to going home? _____ If not, why not?

_____

_____

What do you need to change about your home to make it a place you would look forward to going to?

_____

_____

One person I interviewed said, "I know my living space affects my level of wellness. Where I lived before (an average part of town in a run down complex) depressed me. Now I live in a nice part of town in a public complex with others, but it is neat and modern. I feel much better."

Is your home a safe, comfortable haven from the rest of the world? _____ If not, why not?

_____

_____

What do you need to change about your home to make it a safe, comfortable haven from the rest of the world? _____

_____

I have lived in several places where I did not feel safe. One place was so remote that no one could have helped me if I had needed help. Another was on a busy street where there were frequently altercations in the middle of the night. Both of these places had minimal locks which made me feel even more vulnerable. I now live in a neighborhood where friendly people are close by, with good locks, back-up locking systems and, for extra protection, security and enjoyment, I have a big dog.

Do you feel safe in your home? _____ If not, why not? _____
What could you do so that you feel safe in your home? _____

_____

_____

_____

If you live with others, do you have a space in your home that is just your private space that you can decorate to suit yourself, where you can keep your things, and know that they will not be disturbed, and where you can go to spend time by yourself and be involved in your own activities? _____ If not, why not?

_____

_____

What would you need to do to have such a private space for yourself in your home?

_____

_____

People I have talked to emphasize the importance of a living space that is clean and easy to keep clean and maintain. If you are a "pack rat," this can be difficult. When you give up your need to keep everything, and dispose of things you don't need, your home may feel much more comfortable. Lots of "stuff" around can make living space difficult to keep clean, maintained, and attractive. It can increase stress.
Is your living space easy to clean, and keep clean, attractive to you and easy to maintain? _____ If not, why not?

_____

_____

What do you need to change about your living space to make it easy to clean, and keep clean, attractive to you and easy to maintain?

_____

_____

Accessibility to transportation and services is a high priority for most people. Constant transportation hassles and lack of access to necessary services can make your life difficult and more stressful

Is your living space easily accessible to transportation and services? _____ If not, why not?

_____

_____

What would you have to do to make your home more easily accessible to services?

_____

_____

Some people like to live alone. Others prefer to live with others. A woman I talked to said, ""I have lived in a variety of arrangements over the years. The worst possible arrangement for me is to live alone in a place where I don't know any of my neighbors. For me, isolation leads to devastation. Living with someone who knows you well and knows how to treat you is the best. Currently I reside in a cooperative living arrangement in a membership cooperative. This works well for me. I have the privacy of my room, but whenever I need some companionship I can always go to the lounge."
I prefer to live alone. _____ If so, why?

_____

_____

If you prefer to live alone, and you now live with others, what can you do to change the situation?

_____

_____

I prefer to live with others. _____ If so, why?

_____

_____

If you prefer to live with others, and you now live alone, what can you do to change the situation?

_____

_____

If your living space is not appropriate to your needs or is getting in the way of your wellness and recovery, consider finding a place to live that better suits your needs.

_____ I need to move. Why?

_____

_____

_____

_____

What steps can you take to make that happen?

_____

_____

An enthusiastic woman I interviewed said, " Moving, I went from bounds to LEAPS! I never felt better in my LIFE. A good environment is crucial." I agree.

Lifestyle Issues

Fine Tuning Your Life

The change in my life since I realized that every aspect of my existence affects how I feel is profound.

In talking with people all over the country about mental health issues, and assessing my own experience, I have found that there are some basic lifestyle issues that are usually not addressed when working toward wellness and recovery. This chapter is an attempt to give this subject needed attention.

When you feel out of sorts with the world, you may have a tendency to look for some profound cause, like a serious medical problem, a traumatic experience, or a severe loss. Like others, you may forget to explore the more mundane aspects of your life, your daily living habits, and your activities. People who have gotten well, and stayed well, have taken a closer look at their lives and work on fine tuning the details. For instance, a woman I interviewed said, "When I feel good, I am very active. I work out at the gym, bike, jog, walk, go to movies, spend time with my nieces, bake, write, and read. To make myself happy, I buy myself a new piece of clothing, let myself be lazy, and indulge in reading. I like biographies and autobiographies, fiction and non-fiction."

What activities make you feel better? You may have found that you need to take time during the day to involve yourself in activities that you enjoy. These are the kind of activities in which, once you are involved, you can think of nothing else. The activity completely absorbs you. You may have forgotten about these kinds of activities and how they make you feel, things that you know you do well and where performance is not measured.

In personally addressing this issue, I found that there were activities I had stopped doing long ago, such as playing the piano and sewing, that really make me feel good. In the "busyness" of life, such as raising children and developing a career, these activities were forgotten. They are now part of my wellness tool chest. If I am feeling a little glum, or feeling stressed, I spend some time involved in such an activity. My life feels enriched when I include some of these activities in each day.

Suggestions for activities you might enjoy include: reading a good book, gardening, sewing working with clay, wood working, writing, visiting art galleries or museums, playing with children, playing with pets, cooking, playing games, or watching videos.

My own personal list of activities to include in my schedule on difficult days:

quilting	sewing
playing the piano	drumming
baking bread	writing
painting a picture	reading a good book

Spend some time thinking about activities that you really enjoy. You may want to discuss this with a friend or family members who can help you recall things you enjoyed doing.

What activities totally absorb you and make you feel better?

_____

_____

_____

_____

_____

_____

To convince yourself that it really helps to involve yourself in an absorbing activity, note how you feel before you did one.

_____

_____

_____

How did you feel after you involved yourself in an absorbing activity?

_____

_____

_____

_____ I am committed to involving myself in an absorbing activity from time to time. Why?

_____

_____

_____

Take a Fun Break Taking a fun break is a great way to lift your mood and balance your life. Take time out when things are getting hectic for a fun break. A friend of mine plays with a "Wii," an electronic game, when she needs a break. I take a long walk in the woods with my dog; invite a friend, whose company I enjoy, out for lunch; spend the evening watching a funny video like "The Gods Must Be Crazy" or "The General"; playing paper dolls with my granddaughters; or roller-skating.

Describe a possible fun break.

_____

_____

_____

To convince yourself that it really helps to take a fun break, note how you felt before you took a fun break.

_____

_____

_____

How did you feel after you took a fun break?

_____

_____

_____

____ I am committed to taking fun breaks when I need a lift or feel stressed. Why?

_____

_____

_____

What effect does laughter have on the way you feel?

Researchers have found that one of the least expensive treatments for pent-up anxiety, fear, and frustration is a hearty laugh. Laughter has respiratory effects, filling the lungs with air over and over and providing pulmonary ventilation. It also has a cardiac effects, increasing the heart rate directly proportional to the duration of the laughter. The heart rate then drops below the level of the pre-laughter period. Laughter increases both the systolic and the diastolic blood pressure, but afterwards, there is a drop in pressure below pre-laughter levels. A hearty belly laugh results in almost total body relaxation. Since laughter has so many positive benefits, perhaps we should laugh more often.

Sometimes finding anything to laugh about is difficult. Some laugh instigators include comic strips, jokes, puns, certain movies and videos, and good comedians.

I make it a point to watch several British comedies on television. I get at least several good laughs out of them. The comic strips "Calvin and Hobbes," "For Better or Worse" and "Zits" also tickle my laughter palate.

What makes you laugh?

_____

_____

_____

_____

_____

_____

Next time you laugh, note how you felt before you laughed.

_____

_____

_____

Note how you felt after you laughed.

_____

_____

_____

____ I am going to try and laugh more often. Why?

_____

_____

_____

_____

_____

_____

Pets Many people report amazing positive effects from having a pet in their lives. I never thought a dog would make such a difference in my life. Several years ago, I "dog sat" for my daughter's dog while she was traveling. By the time she came home, I knew I had to have a dog. With an animal there is always something to smile about. I can never feel too grumpy. It has taken care of my problems with sticking to my exercise routine. And I rest easier because I assume that most people will not bother a dog or the accompanying human being. They are always there for you, even when you are in a "slump" and you feel like the rest of the world is against you.

People who have pets cited many advantages. If you have a pet, which of the following are true for you?

       ____ Petting an animal is relaxing.
       ____ Pets are not critical, threatening or judgmental.

_____ Pets keep my attention on the positive aspects of life.

_____ Pets reduce stress.

_____ My pet keeps me smiling.

_____ My pet improves my state of mind, so that when I return to more pressing concerns I can put them in better perspective and cope more appropriately.

_____ Pets have increased my ability to develop rapport with other people.

_____ Pets encourage me to interact with other people.

_____ When walking with a pet, others pay attention.

_____ Pets are fun.

_____ Pets love you unconditionally.

_____ Pets don't care what mood you are in.

_____ Pets don't try to change you.

_____ Pets love to be loved, touched, and held.

_____ Pets release tension.

_____ Pets convince you that you are lovable.

_____ Pets give life purpose and meaning.

_____ Pets encourage play and laughter.

_____ Pets force you to get your exercise.

Other ways your pet is helpful to you:

_____

_____

_____

Dogs and cats are the most popular pets. However, guinea pigs (which are very affectionate and will cuddle on your lap all evening), rabbits, birds and fish are also popular.

_____ I have a pet.

_____ I am going to get a pet. If so, why?

_____

_____

_____

In many rental housing units, pets are not allowed, even though you know that a well- managed and maintained pet is no more dirty or offensive than your average run-of-the-mill human being. Sometimes a landlord will make an exception if you have been a good tenant, or will allow a smaller pet such as a guinea pig or a bird.

Not everyone likes animals or enjoys pets. Don't force yourself, or anyone else, to get a pet if they are really not comfortable with the idea.

_____ I am not going to get a pet. If not, why not?

_____

_____

_____

Animal shelters are an inexpensive source of pets, especially dogs and cats. When you get a pet from such a shelter, the animal is usually in good condition, has been carefully checked for medical problems and received necessary shots. The shelter will provide you with information on the animal's care.

Water Many of us have been told to take a long, hot bath when we were having a hard time. You may have regarded it as a simplistic solution to a major problem. And in many cases it is just that. But many of people use water, such as a shower, bath, whirlpool, hot tub, or pool, as a soothing part of their routine, because, in addition to being part of their hygiene routine, it makes them feel better. You might take time out during the day, if things get hectic, or if you are feeling discouraged, to give your body the benefit of the calming properties of water.

I had not really considered the therapeutic effects of water on how I feel until several years ago. Before that, a morning or evening shower was just one more hurried part of my daily routine. It was my birthday, on a cold and snowy day in January. I was trying to think of something nice I could do for myself. I decided a swim in a heated pool would be just the thing. I called a local motel with an indoor pool and they said that, while they usually only allow people to swim who are in the motel, or have a monthly membership, since it was my birthday they would make an exception. For $6.00, I spent a delicious afternoon, going between the pool and whirlpool, lazily watching the snow fall on the glass roof. I felt so good afterward that I purchased a membership and gave myself this treat several times a week. I relaxed and got my exercise at the same time.

Many community-based recreational centers, motels, and Y's allow easy, inexpensive access to water facilities. In my community, the local mental health center has reserved time at a motel so people can go swimming who feel self-conscious when the facility is open to the public. If this is something you think you would enjoy, explore the possibilities in your community and see if you can fit them in your budget.

_____ I am going to explore the possibility of using a swimming facility.

You don't have to go to a pool, or get a membership, to enjoy the benefits of water. Your own bathtub or shower can suffice.

There are even inexpensive whirlpool units which give you a sense of luxury and relaxation in your own tub.

_____ I already use water to relax me and make me feel better.

_____ I am going to explore using water to relax me and make me feel better. I am going to do that by:

_____

_____

Most people find warm water most relaxing. However, others find cooler temperatures work best for them.

_____ I prefer warm temperatures.

_____ I prefer cool temperatures.

To get a sense of how water affects you, complete the following before and after your next "water experience."

What I did _____ For how long _____

How I felt before I did it.

_____

_____

How I felt after I did it.

_____

_____

Color Many people find color considerations, both in decorating their homes, the clothes they wear, and the things they look at to have an affect how they feel. I know that a very light shade of pink, almost a white with just a little red coloring added to it, has a very soothing effect on me. I painted all the walls in an apartment I rented this color and it felt great, and had a positive affect on my mood. Others have reported a similar experience with a light shade of pink.

What colors make you feel best when you wear them?

_____

_____

When you are buying yourself new clothes, focus on these colors. When you are having a day when you feel down, wear clothing in these colors. It will help perk you up.

Every time you look in the mirror it will give you a lift.

Notice the color of the walls and decor and in those rooms where you feel best. What are they?

_____

_____

When decorating your own space, use these colors. If you are living in a space where the colors make you feel down, yet you can't afford to redecorate, try an inexpensive alternative, like just painting a wall or two, or using a brightly-colored coverlet from a rummage sale. It can make a big difference. If your workspace is being redecorated, make your color preferences known. Let your employer know the colors that make you feel best.

Music Many people find particular kinds of music to be relaxing. However, the kind of music varies according to personal preference. Some people prefer classical, while others prefer the new-age type of music, jazz, folk, rock, big band, hip hop or country. Whatever the music, it needs to be something you like. If you don't like it, it won't relax you.

Research indicates that for music to relieve stress, it should have 60-70 beats per minute.

What kind of music makes you feel better?

_____

_____

Go through your music collection and make a note of those pieces that make you feel more relaxed and peaceful. If you have an IPod or play music on your computer, you may want to combine particular selections on a play list for use when you are feeling down or harried.

Lifestyle Issues

Finishing Up

You have now worked your through this book of concepts, strategies, ideas and tools. It is my hope that this has helped you take "giant steps" in your recovery journey. Before you finish, there are three more areas you may need to consider: strengths, accomplishments and gratitude.

Although you can use the space in this book to write these lists, I suggest you get a loose-leaf binder, binder paper and a set of tabs to keep track of these important topics. Make a tab for each topic: Strengths, Accomplishments and Gratitude. Insert paper as needed behind each tab. Then you can easily add to the lists as you learn more about yourself, as your life changes, and as you recover. You may want to use this binder to keep lists and writing from other sections of this book, like Boosting Your Self-esteem and Journaling. It could be the same binder where you keep your WRAP®, or a different binder. Keep this binder in a place where it is easily accessible so you can review it often and make additions or changes from time to time.

Strengths You have many strengths and positive attributes you bring to this journey that will assist you and support you along the way. It is important to make note of them and review them from time to time, especially when you are coming up against something that is difficult, like a big loss or disappointment, and remind yourself that you have "what it takes" to keep moving forward. Reviewing your responses in the Journaling and Boosting your Self-esteem chapters will help you in identifying your strengths.

Strengths that others have shared included the following:
> I have strong compassion, especially for children, animals and people who are struggling.
> I have gotten through lots of difficult times.
> When I am faced with a challenge, I work hard to resolve it in a way that is best for me.
> I am optimistic about my recovery and the future.
> I control my temper.
> I am smart. I got good grades in school and understand new ideas quickly.
> I am creative. I can think of lots of different ways to do things.
> I am patient. I am willing to wait for things that I know are right.
> I am responsible. If I say I will do something, others can count on me to do it.
> I take good care of myself in every way.

I have maintained a reasonable weight.

I take good care of my pet.

I am a neat and tidy person.

I am a great parent.

I am a great sister (brother, uncle, aunt, cousin).

I am physically strong.

I have made it through lots of hard times in my life.

I enjoy helping others.

I manage my diabetes well.

Others often turn to me for advice.

I am a good cook.

I like to read. I spend lots of time reading.

I always keep up with my health care appointments.

I keep track of my medications.

Make a list of your strengths. It can be as long as you want. Review this list regularly. I suggest you post a copy on your refrigerator door, a bulletin board or some other place where you can easily see it and review it from time to time. Reviewing this list may be a good Wellness Tool for you. It really helps me when I am upset about something that has happened to me (triggered), or I have Early Warning Signs.

My Strengths

_____

_____

_____

_____

_____

_____

_____

_____

_____

Accomplishments In your life you have accomplished a great deal. There may be some things that are actually huge accomplishments that you don't even count. Make a list here of the amazing accomplishments of your life so you can review them from time to time.

The following accomplishments, shared by others, may give you some ideas.

I made it through that deep depression.

I have learned how to talk back to the voices in my head.

I used to always think I was stupid. Now I know I am really smart.